Just Right

Carol Lethaby   Ana Acevedo
Jeremy Harmer

Workbook
with answer key

Photo acknowledgements

p.8 ©Reza Estakhrian/Stone/Getty Images; p.15 ©Helene Rogers/Alamy, ©Stockdisc Premium/Alamy; p.39 a ©Lesley Sandles/Alamy, b ©KPA/CBI/Sven Hoogerhuis/Content Mine International/Alamy, c ©M J Kim/Reportage/Getty Images, d ©Craig Lovell/Eagle Visions Photography/Alamy, p.40 t ©Sipa Press/Rex Features, b ©Allstar Picture Library/Alamy; p.46 ©Royalty Free/Corbis; p.49 ©Stuart Dee/Alamy,; p.53 ©KPA Honorar & Belege/Content Mine International/Alamy; p.60 ©WizData Inc./Alamy; p.62 ©Phil Wigglesworth/Alamy; p.66 ©Blend Images/Getty Images; p.68 ©Gary Roebuck/Alamy; p.69 ©Chloe Johnson/Alamy

First published 2007 by Marshall Cavendish Education
Reprinted 2008

Marshall Cavendish Education is a member of the Times Publishing Group

Marshall Cavendish Education
5th Floor
32–38 Saffron Hill
London
EC1N 8FH
www.mcelt.com/justright

Designed by Hart McLeod Ltd, Cambridge
Illustrations by Jo Taylor, Yane Christiansen, Francis Fung, Rory Walker, Valeryia Steadman, Tim Oliver, Stephanie Thelwell

ISBN: 978-0-462-00779-3

Printed and bound by Times Offset (M) Sdn. Bhd. Malaysia

Contents

Function: introducing someone

1 Put the words in the correct order to make sentences.

a 1 to / you / Nice/meet / . /
Debbie / name's / my / . /

Nice to meet you.
My name's Debbie.

2 too / to / you / Nice / Debbie /
meet / . / , /

....

....

3 I'm / Hi! / Suzie / . /

....

....

b 1 Hello / you / How / Jenny / . /
are / ? / ....

....

2 this / Jenny / is / Mum and /
Dad /. / , /......................................

....

3 meet / you / Pleased / to / . /
Jenny /..

....

2 Write the sentences in Activity 1 in the correct order to make two conversations.

a SUZI:...

DEBBIE:...

....

SUZI:..

....

b JIM:...

....

MUM:..

....

DAD:..

....

3 Have a conversation with Helena and Marco.

HELENA: Hello. I'm Helena. What's your name?

YOU: *My name's* ....

HELENA: Nice to meet you.

YOU: ....

HELENA: This is my friend Marco.

YOU: ....

MARCO: Hi. How are you?

YOU: ....

🔊 Listen to Track 1. Say your lines after the beep.

Grammar: subject pronouns, verb *be* (affirmative)

4 Match the phrases. Write them in the spaces.

I am ◆ my name is ◆ he's ◆ they are ◆ we are ◆ he is ◆
you are ◆ we're ◆ my name's ◆ I'm ◆ they're ◆ it's ◆ she's ◆
you're ◆ it is ◆ she is

a ......*I am*...... ......*I'm*......

b ....

c ....

d ....

e ....

f ....

g ....

h ....

5 Complete the sentences.

I'm. Carole. This .... Yusef and this
.... Nadia. They' .... my friends.
He'........... nice and she'........... nice too. The name of
my school .... The Just Right School of
English. It'........... a good school and the teachers
.... very good too. Yusef, Nadia and I
.... in the same class.

Vocabulary: useful phrases

6 Complete the conversation with phrases from the box.

> thank you. ◆ That's OK. ◆ Excuse me.
> Sorry! I don't understand.

a

b Yes?

c You dropped your book.

d ....

e Here's your book.

f Oh, ...

g ....

7 Say the names of the letters. Think about the pronunciation. Circle the letters that are different.

A H J I
B C D E F G P V X
K Q U W
Y I T
L M N R S

Which two letters are missing?

Listen to Track 2 to check your answers.

8 Listen to Track 3. Spell the words.

1 _ _   2 _ _ _ _   3 _ _ _ _
4 _ _ _ _   5 _ _ _   6 _ _ _   7 _ _ _
8 _ _   9 _ _ _ _ _   10 _ _ _   11 _ _

9 Write out a three-line conversation with the words. You need to use two of the words twice. Listen to Track 4 to check your answers.

MAN: ....

YOUNG MAN: ....

YOUNG WOMAN: ....

How did you do?

10 Translate these sentences into your language.

a What's your name?

....

b Pleased to meet you.

....

c Peter and Ian are friends.

....

d Who's your teacher?

....

e Who are your friends?

....

Phonetics

11 Look at the phonemic symbols in the booklet. Write these words in normal spelling.

a /huː/ ....

b /wɒt/ ....

c /ðɪs/ ....

d /aɪm/ ....

e /ðeɪə/ ....

Listen to Track 5 to check your answers.

UNIT 2 Where are you from?

Vocabulary: colours, countries, nationalities

1 Look at the names of the countries. Write the nationality words in the correct box according to the spelling.

> Australia ◆ Brazil ◆ Canada ◆ China ◆ France ◆ Japan ◆ Korea
> Mexico ◆ ~~Russia~~ ◆ South Africa ◆ The UK ◆ The USA

-ian	-an	-ese	-ch or -sh
Russian			

2 Write the colours.

a _yellow_ and _____ = orange
b _____ and _____ = grey
c _____ and _____ = pink
d _____ and _____ = green
e _____ and _____ = brown

Grammar: verb *be* (negative and interrogative)

3 Look at the pictures. Correct the statements.

Example: Madonna's Australian. She isn't Australian.
She's American.

Flag - The UK

Kimonos - Japan

Pizza - Italy

Boomerangs - Australia

Pyramids - Mexico

you-?

a Kimonos are Korean.
b Boomerangs are from South Africa.
c The pyramids are in Russia.
d The flag is French.
e Pizza's from France.
f You're British.

4 Complete the conversations.

Conversation 1

BOB: Where ___are___ you ___from___, Richard?

RICHARD: I'_____ Australian.

BOB: _____ you _____ Sydney?

RICHARD: No, I'_____. I'm _____ Melbourne.

BOB: _____ Melbourne near Sydney?

RICHARD: Yes, _____. Well, it _____ very far.

BOB: _____ Sydney the capital of Australia?

RICHARD: No, it _____. It'_____ Canberra.

BOB: _____ nice?

RICHARD: I don't know!

Conversation 2

JILL: Are Tina and Carlos in your class?

LUPE: No, _____. They'_____ in a different class but we'_____ friends.

JILL: _____ you all _____ Argentina?

LUPE: No, we _____. Tina and I _____ from Argentina but Carlos _____. He'_____from Venezuela.

5 Complete and answer the questions.

a Who ......*are*...... you?

You: I' ....

b Where .... you .... ?

You: I' ....

c What' .... your nationality?

You: I'...

d .... colour' .... the flag of your country?

You: It'...

e What .... the names of the countries near your country?

You: ....

f What colour .... their flags?

You: ....

g .... your favourite colour?

You: ....

h Really? That'................ my favourite colour too!

Listen to Track 6. Read your lines after the beep.

Function: greetings

6 Write conversations for the three situations. Use language from the box.

> I'm very well, thank you. ◆ Fine, thanks. ◆ Not bad. Good morning, afternoon, evening. ◆ Hello. ◆ Hi! And you? ◆ You? ◆ How are you? ◆ How's it going?

a (10.00 p.m.) Greet Mrs. Wells, an old teacher.

Good evening Mrs Wells.

....

b (3.00 p.m.) Greet a good friend.

....

....

c (8.00 p.m.) Greet a neighbour.

....

....

Pronunciation: word stress (countries and nationality words)

7 Say the words. Underline the stressed syllable in the names of the countries.

a Australia b Brazil c Canada d China
e Japan f Korea g Mexico h Russia

Listen to Track 7 to check your answers.

8 Say the words. Match the nationalities according to their stress.

Mexican	Korean
Australian	Brazilian
British	(South) African
Canadian	Russian

What three nationalities have a different stress from the name of the country?

How did you do?

9 Find the mistakes in these sentences and correct them below.

a Where you are from?

....

b Tom's from Australian.

....

c You are British?

....

d Is your country nice? Yes, is.

....

e I amn't American.

....

Phonetics

10 Look at the phonemic symbols in the booklet. Write these words from Unit 2 in normal spelling.

a /kəˈriːən/...

b /ɒˈstreɪliən/...

c /ˈkʌlə/...

d /aːnt/...

e /ɪznt/...

Listen to Track 8 to check your answers.

UNIT 3 What's your job?

Vocabulary: jobs and occupations

1 **Guess the jobs and write them in the spaces and circles.**

   a Pete and Claire are OO_ OO_ _ _ in a school. They teach English.

   b Sara and Martha are _ _ _ O _ _ O _ . They clean offices.

   c Bono's the _ O _ _ _ _ in the band U2.

   d Madonna is a singer and a good _ OOO_ _ .

   e I'm an OOO _ _ , like Scarlet Johansson and Brad Pitt.

   f Aldo's a O_ O_ in a restaurant.

   g Dan's a _ O_ _ _ in a hospital.

   h What do you do? We're _ O_ _ _ OO_ at university.

2 **Complete the dialogues. Use the letters in the circles in Activity 1 to find the occupations.**

...Are..... you .....an..... engineer?

No, I ....

What .... you .... ?

I'm an ....

.... you .... architect?

No, ...

What'................ your .... ?

I'm ....

3 **Write occupations. Use a/an. Then write an example of people you know.**

Example: *An engineer – My friend's an engineer.*
A doctor – Alan Ashby's a doctor.

....

....

....

....

Grammar: *a, an,* possessive adjectives

4 **Complete the sentences with *a* or *an* only when necessary.**

   a Gill's ...a... singer.

   b Bob's .... architect.

   c Jamie and Ray are .... cooks.

   d Tomoko's .... Japanese.

   e Moira's .... engineer.

   f Colin's .... computer programmer.

5 **Fill in the blanks with a possessive adjective (*my, your, his, her, its, our, their*).**

Rachel, Thomas and I are friends. We work in a hospital. I'm a doctor. (**a**) ....My..... job is interesting. Rachel and Thomas are nurses. (**b**) .... job is interesting too. (**c**) .... hospital is very big. (**d**) .... name is Stafford Memorial Hospital.
Rachel is a good cook but it isn't her job; it's (**e**) .... hobby. Thomas is a good singer. (**f**) .... songs are nice. What's (**g**) .... job?

6 Circle the correct words in the sentences.

a They're/**Their** job is interesting.
They're/Their engineers.
b This is Kuba. It's/Its a nice cat.
This is my cat. It's/Its name is Kuba.
c You're/Your a teacher.
You're/Your teacher is South African.
d He's/His a baker.
He's/His job is difficult.

7 Write the numbers.

a 9 _nine_   b 19 ....

c 3 ....   d 13 ....

e 5 ....   f 15 ....

g 11 ....   h 12 ....

Function: personal information

8 You want to go to a gym. Write the receptionist's questions. Then answer the questions with your personal information.

YOU: Hello. Can I have some information about the gym?

RECEPTIONIST: Sure. What's your first name?

YOU: _It's_ ....

RECEPTIONIST: Right. (last name?)

.... ?

YOU: ....

RECEPTIONIST: (telephone number?)

.... ?

YOU: ....

RECEPTIONIST: (email?)

.... ?

YOU: Yes. It's ....

RECEPTIONIST: OK. I'll send you the information right away.

YOU: ....

🔊 Listen to Track 9. Say your lines after the beep.

Pronunciation: /ə/ (schwa)

9 Say the sentences. Underline the letters that have the sound /ə/, like *the* /ðə/.

a Danny's <u>a</u> dan<u>cer</u>.
b Pat's an accountant.
c Len's a taxi driver.
d Is Kim a singer?
e She isn't a painter.

🔊 Listen to Track 10 to check your answers.

How did you do?

10 Translate these sentences into your language.

a What do you do?

....

b What's your job?

....

c Tracy's a doctor.

....

d We're students.

....

e I'm not a singer. I'm a dancer.

....

Phonetics

11 Look at the phonemic symbols in the booklet. Write these words from Unit 3 in normal spelling.

a /dʒɒb/ ....

b /əˈkaʊntənt/ ....

c /striːt/ ....

d /stjuːdənt/ ....

e /tiːtʃə/ ....

🔊 Listen to Track 11 to check your answers.

UNIT 4 Families

Function: talking about age

1 Work out the ages. Complete the sentences.

Lucy 2006

1924

Saturday

You?

Daniel 1950

a How old is your house? It's __82__ years old.

b _____ old _____ Lucy? _____ old.

c _____ you?

I _____ .

d How _____ is Daniel? He' _____ .

e _____ old _____ the dogs? Only _____ .

Vocabulary: family members

2 Read the text. True or False?

a Nathalie has one sister.	T	Ⓕ
b Nathalie's parents are from Peru.	T	F
c Alicia and Alberto have seven grandchildren.	T	F
d Nathalie has two uncles.	T	F
e Nathalie has three brothers.	T	F

My name's Nathalie. I'm 20 years old. My family is large. I am one of five children, two girls and three boys.

My mum has three sisters, Elvira, Tessa and Sylvia. They are married and have two children each. Mum also has two brothers, Ralph and Nick. They are not married.

Elvira and her husband Pat are our neighbours. They have two daughters, Emma and Merce. They are 19 and 21. We are good friends.

My mum's parents, Alicia and Alberto are from Peru.

3 Write the family relationships.

a Elvira is Nathalie's __aunt__ .

b Alberto is her _____ .

c Ralph, Nick and Pat are her _____ .

d Ralph and Nick are _____ .

e Emma and Merce are _____ .

f Emma, Merce and Nathalie are _____ .

g Alicia and Alberto have two _____ .

h Elvira and Pat are _____ and

_____ .

Grammar: demonstratives (*this, that, these, those*)

4 Label the pictures with these words: *this, that, these, those*.

a .... b ....

c .... d ....

5 Underline the correct word.

a Are <u>these</u>/those your parents on this photo?
b Look at this/that man in that car. Is it Brad Pitt?
c Are those/this your glasses over here?
d Those/That jeans in that shop are nice.
e What's this/that thing on your head?

6 Fill in the blanks with *this, that, these, those*.

a Look at ......<u>those</u>...... boys in the park.
b Who's .... over there?
c .... is my friend Laura. Laura, this is Tim.
d .... is an easy exercise.
e Who are .... people over there?
f Come here and look at .... pictures.
g What's .... in the tree? A cat. I think.
h .... children in this photo are my cousins.

Pronunciation: /d/ and /ð/

7 Say the sentences. Write in the words underlined according to their sound /d/ or /ð/.

a <u>Frida</u> and <u>Nadia</u> are <u>mother</u> and <u>daughter</u>.
b <u>Fred</u>'s a <u>good</u> <u>brother</u>.
c <u>Their</u> <u>father</u>'s over <u>there</u>.
d <u>Read</u> <u>this</u> <u>today</u> and <u>that</u> on <u>Monday</u>.

Words with /d/	Words with /ð/
Frida	

🔊 Listen to Track 12 to check your answers.

How did you do?

8 Find the mistakes in these sentences and correct them below.

a How old you are?
....?

b What's this in your hand?
....?

c This people are nice.
....

d That pictures are new.
....

e Is those your keys?
....?

Phonetics

9 Look at the phonemic symbols in the booklet. Write these words from Unit 4 in normal spelling.

a /sʌn/...
b /jɪəz/...
c /ˈkʌzn/...
d /ðiːz/...
e /ðis/...

🔊 Listen to Track 13 to check your answers.

Review Units 1–4

Grammar and functions

1 Write the questions in the correct place in the dialogue.

Who is she?   Who are you?
Where's Mona O'Hara?

Super agent Blond, part 1

JIM: Hello agent 999.

BEN: Sorry? I'm not an agent. My name's Ben Murphy. I'm a taxi driver. **a** _Who are you_ ?

JIM: I'm Blond, Jim Blond. Hey,

b _____ ?

BEN: Mona O'Hara? **c** _____ ?

JIM: Come on Murphy, you know. She's our woman in Cambridge, of course.

2 Ben introduces Lara to Jim. Complete the dialogue.

Super agent Blond, part 2

JIM: Ah, here is Mona. Good evening, Mona.

BEN: She isn't Mona. She's my friend Lara. Lara, **a** _this is Jim Blond_ . **b** _____ .

LARA: That's interesting. **c** _____ you, Jim.

JIM: Nice to meet you too, Mona. You're very young! **d** _____ ?

LARA: I'm 17 years old. **e** _____ .

JIM: Agents are very young these days.

3 Jim and Lara talk about their nationalities. Complete the conversation.

Super agent Blond, part 3

JIM: Where **a** _are you from_ ?

LARA: I'm **b** _Lara_ _____ Australia. You're American, right?

JIM: Of course not! **c** _____ British. **d** _____ is Murphy from?

e _____ Australian too?

LARA: Ben? No, **f** _____ .

g _____ Canada.

JIM: Ah, Canadian. Canadians are good agents.

4 Fill in the blanks with *this*, *that*, *these* and *those*.

Super agent Blond, part 4

JIM: Look at a _those_ people over there.

LARA: Oh, are they your friends?

JIM: Shhh! No, they aren't. They're Lorry and Harry. They're really bad. And **b** _____ 's their car.

LARA: Well, **c** _____ is our car. And **d** _____ are the keys. Come on, let's go.

BEN: No, Lara! Look Jim, we aren't really agents.

LARA: We are now!

5 Read the four parts of Super agent Blond.

a Find examples of the indefinite article *a* or *an* and underline them.

b Find five possessive pronouns.

))) Listen to Track 14–17 to check all your answers.

6 You are Blond. Ask Lara questions to complete the form. You need to write six questions.

Application form for new agents

First name: _____ Last name: _____

Nationality: _____ Age: _____

Address: _____

_____

Telephone number: _____

Email: _____

1 What's your first name?

_____

_____

_____

_____

))) Listen to Track 18. Ask your questions after the beep. Write Lara's answers in the form.

Review: Vocabulary

WORD LIST

accountant   actor   address   age   architect   American   aunt
Australia   Australian   baby   baker   black   blue   Brazil   Brazilian
British   brother   bus driver   Bye!   Canada   Canadian   car
Caribbean   class   cleaner   China   Chinese   colour   computer-
programmer   conversation   cook   country   cousin   dancer
daughter   dentist   doctor   drawings   email (address)   engineer
Excuse me.   father   first name   flag   France   French   friend
glasses   grandchild   grandfather   grandmother   green   house
husband   I don't understand.   introductions   Jamaica   Japan
Japanese   jeans   job   keys   Korea   Korean   last name   map
Mexico   Mexican   month   mother   name   nationality   neighbour
North America   nurse   occupation   painter   parents   people
photo   red   Russia   Russian   See you later!   singer   sister   son
Sorry!   Sorry?   South Africa   South African   South America   student
taxi driver   teacher   telephone number   today   The UK   The USA
Thank you.   That's OK.   uncle   watch   white   wife   year   yellow

7 Make a vocabulary notebook.

Make a 'Useful expressions' page. Find seven useful expressions in the word list. Write the expressions and a translation in your language.

Example: - Thank you. (Gracias)
- That's OK. (de nada)

When you find new expressions add them to this page.

8 Writing new words in groups can help you remember them. Copy and complete the boxes with words from the word list.

Countries	Nationalities	Occupations	Family members	
Australia	Australian	an engineer a doctor	Male grandfather	Female grandmother

Make a new group for 'Colours'. You can write a translation next to the words, if you want.

Review: Pronunciation

9 Complete the series of letters. Think of their sound!

A B C D E F G H I J K L M N
O P Q R S T U V W X Y Z

a   A, H, J ....

b   B, C, ...

c   F, L, ...

d   Q, ...

Listen to Track 19 to check your answers.

10 a Find the names of three countries and three nationality words in the sentences. Underline the stressed syllables.

1   My brother's a doctor, like my father.
2   My mother and my dad are from Canada. They're Canadian.
3   My friend's a dentist in Japan. He's British but his wife and daughter are Japanese.
4   These red watches are from China but those aren't Chinese. They're from the USA.

Listen to Track 20 to check your answers.

b Complete the table below with words from the sentences.

Words with /ə/ brother
Words with /d/ doctor
Words with /ð/ brother

Listen to Track 21 to check your answers. Practise saying the sentences.

UNIT 5 Time

Function: Telling the time

1 Put the words in the correct order to make questions.

a It's 12 o'clock midday in London. What / is / time / it / in San Francisco / ? / ...... What time is it in San Francisco? ....

b It's 3.15 p.m. in London. What / the / 's / time / in Mexico City?
....

c It's 4.45 a.m in Buenos Aires. in / Paris / time / it / is / What / ? /
....

d It's 6.30 p.m. in Beijing, China. time / in Sydney / ? / is / What / it / ....

e It's 9.03 a.m. in New York. the / time / in Sao Paulo / What / 's /? / ....

f It's 7.20 p.m. in London. in your country / time / What / it / is / ? / ....

2 Look at the map. Work out the times and answer the questions in Activity 1.

Example: It's twelve midday in London.
What time is it in San Francisco?

a It's four o'clock in the morning.

b ....
....

c ....
....

d ....
....

e ....
....

f ....
....

Map:
LONDON 1200 GMT
SAN FRANCISCO, USA -8
NEW YORK, USA -5
PARIS, FRANCE +1
BEIJING, CHINA +8
MEXICO CITY MEXICO -6
SAO PAOLO, BRAZIL -3
BUENOS AIRES, ARGENTINA -4
SYDNEY, AUSTRALIA +10

Vocabulary: everyday actions

3 Make ten true sentences.

Example: I don't work in an office every day.

| I (don't) | go
have
read
watch
work | in an office
to work
breakfast
a book
a shower
in a shop
to bed
television
the paper
DVDs | (at + time).

(on Sundays).

(every day). |

4 Chat with Stella. Write answers.

Hi! I'm Stella, from Manchester, in the UK. Where are you from?

a You: ....
....

In Britain we work from 9.00 to 5.00. What about you?

b You: ....
....

I go to work by bus. People here read the paper or a book on the bus. What about you?

c **You:** ....

Here shops open from 10.00 to 6.00.
I go shopping on Saturdays or Sundays. And you?

d **You:** ....

I go to my Spanish class on Wednesdays from 6.00
to 8.00. When is your English class?

e **You:** ....

Well, nice to meet you. Bye.

f **You:** ....

◁))) **Listen to Track 22. Talk to Stella. Say your lines after the beep.**

Grammar: present simple (affirmative and negative)

5   **Fill in the blanks with the correct present simple form of the verbs in brackets.**

Many people in Britain a ...._read_.... (read) the paper in the morning, at breakfast or on the bus or train. Milan and Neela Joshi are newsagents. They sell newspapers and magazines. Neela **b** .... (get up) at 5.00. She **c** .... (have) a shower but she **d** .... (not have) breakfast. She takes the papers to lots of houses at 6.30 every morning, Sundays too.

Milan **e** .... (get up) at 6.30 and **f** .... (open) the shop at 8.00. They **g** .... (close) the shop at 9.00 p.m. In the evening they **h** .... (relax). Milan **i** .... (watch) television and Neela **j** .... (read) the papers! They **k** .... (not see) their friends in the week, only on Sunday afternoon. 'We work very hard', says Neela, 'but we like our job!'

6   **True or false?**

a   Many people in Britain read the paper in the evening.   T   F

b   Neela reads the papers in the morning.   T   F

c   Milan works in the shop.   T   F

d   He opens the shop at 7.00.   T   F

e   The Joshis work from 6.00 a.m. to 8.00 p.m.   T   F

f   They work on Sunday afternoon too.   T   F

g   Neela has breakfast after her shower.   T   F

Pronunciation: present simple endings /s/, /z/ and /ɪz/

7   **Say the sentences. Write the verbs in the correct place in the table, according to the sound of the endings.**

a   Peter watches television and Sue reads the paper.

b   Ken works all day and relaxes in the evening.

c   Sue puts the baby in its bed, she kisses it and then goes to bed.

d   She sleeps and she gets up when the baby cries.

/s/	/z/	/ɪz/
	reads	watches

◁))) **Listen to Track 23 to check your answers. Say the sentences.**

How did you do?

8   **Translate these sentences into your language.**

a   What time is it? ....

b   It's half past two. ....

c   I go to my English class on Tuesdays and Thursdays.

....

Phonetics

9   **Write these words from Unit 5 in normal spelling.**

a   /dʌznt/ ....

b   /gəʊz/ ....

c   /'mɪnɪts/ ....

d   /dəʊnt/ ....

e   /'wenzdeɪ/ ....

◁))) **Listen to Track 24 to check your answers.**

Vocabulary: food and drink

1 Cross out the word that is different.

a tea   coffee   juice   ~~cake~~
b cheese   milk   chicken   ice cream
c cake   soda   sandwich   bread
d vegetables   salad   fruit   crisps
e chocolate   crisps   eggs   sweets
f fish   chocolate   sweets   cake

2 Chat with Stella. Answer her questions.

STELLA: It's 1 o'clock- lunchtime! In Britain we have a small meal at lunch and a big meal in the evening. What about your country?

YOU: ....

STELLA: I like to have tea, milk and bread for breakfast. And you?

YOU: ....

STELLA: What about lunch? I like a sandwich and some fruit.

YOU: ....

STELLA: Dinner is at seven. We have meat or fish and vegetables. What about you?

YOU: ....

STELLA: I like snacks in the afternoon, chocolate for example. How about you?

YOU: ....

STELLA: Back to work now. Talk to you soon!

🔊 Listen to Track 25. Talk to Stella. Speak after the beep.

3 Copy and complete the lists with words in this section.

Drinks
tea

Snacks
crisps

Breakfast foods
bread

Lunch foods
sandwich

Dinner foods
red meat

When you find new food words, add them to your lists.

Grammar: present simple (*yes/no* questions and short answers)

4 Read the information. Write the names of the people.

This person:
a doesn't eat meat, red or white.
____Raj____
b eats meat every day. ....
c drinks tea. ....
d eats bread at lunch. ....
e has soup for breakfast. ....
f eats vegetables at the
  three meals. ....
g likes crisps. ....

Maiko (Japan) Breakfast: soup, rice and egg or fish. Lunch and dinner: fish or chicken only (one day a week), rice, vegetables and fruit. Drink: Green tea, soda

Sandy (USA) Breakfast: milk, bread and eggs. Lunch: hamburger or sandwich, crisps. Dinner: meat or chicken with vegetables. Drink: coffee, soda

Raj (India) Breakfast: rice, vegetables, pulses (e.g. beans and lentils),fruit. Lunch and dinner: vegetables in different sauces, different kinds of bread and pulses. Drink: yoghurt drink, water

5 Write questions and answers about the people in Activity 4.

a Maiko/meat?

Does Maiko eat meat? Yes, she does.

b Sandy/fish?

.... ? ....

c Maiko and Raj/meat?

.... ? ....

d Maiko/bread?

.... ? ....

e Maiko/Raj/a lot of rice?

.... ? ....

6 Unscramble the words to write questions.

a Do / eat / people in this country / for breakfast / eggs / ? /

.... Yes, they do.

b they / Do / like / a lot of meat / to eat / ? /

.... No, they don't.

c a lot of coffee / drink / Do / they / ? /

.... No, they don't.

d have / a lot of / fish / Do / they / ? /

.... Yes, they do.

e like / they / rice / Do / ? /

.... Yes, they do.

Which country are the questions about?

....

Pronunciation: intonation in *yes/no* questions

7 Listen to these questions on Track 26. Does the intonation go up or down?

a What do you like for lunch?   up (down)

b Do you eat snacks?   up down

c Do you like fish?   up down

d Does your family eat together?   up down

e Do people in your country eat rice?   up down

Which question is different? Why? Practise saying the questions with the correct intonation.

Function: ordering food

8 Look at the waiter's notes. Order the food.

Table 3   Waiter: Bob.

Cheese sandwich, chocolate ice-cream, coffee (milk, no sugar)

Waiter: Can I help you?

a *I'd like a cheese sandwich and a chocolate ice cream, please* .

Waiter: What would you like to drink?

b ....

Waiter: Anything else?

c ....

Waiter: That's £5.20, please.

Listen to Track 27 to check your answers.

9 Now you are the waiter. Listen to Track 28. Ask the questions in Activity 8 after the beep. Write the person's order.

How did you do?

10 Find the mistakes in these sentences and correct them below.

a Does Sandy likes meat?

.... ?

b Yes, she likes.

....

c You like rice?

....

d No, I no like.

....

Phonetics

11 Look the phonemic symbols in the booklet. Write these words from Unit 6 in normal spelling.

a /ˈɒrɪndʒ/ ....

b /dʒuːs/ ....

c /ˈfɪʃənˈtʃɪps/ ....

d /təˈmaːtəʊ/ ....

e /ˈbredənˈbʌtə/ ....

Listen to Track 29 to check your answers.

UNIT 7 Free time

Vocabulary: Hobbies

1 Find the names of different hobbies in this puzzle. Be careful! There are some extra words and letters.

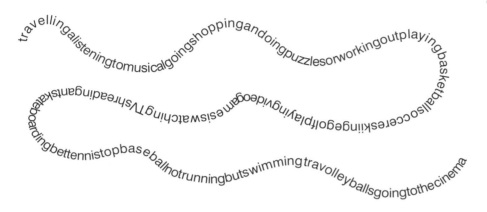

2 Write the words in the correct column.

sports	hobbies you can do by yourself	hobbies you have to do with other people
Swimming		

3 Look at the table and write sentences about the people.

Jane ♥	Marie ♥	Kevin and Trudy ♥

a Jane likes soccer.

b ....

c ....

d ....

e ....

f ....

Grammar: present simple (*Wh-* questions)

4 Put these words in the right order to make questions and answers.

a do / What / free / you / time / do / your / in / ?

   What do you do in
   your free time?

   go / movies / I / often / the / to / .

   ....

   ....

b go / with / Who / you / do / ?

   ....

   ....

   usually / go / friend / with / I / my / .

   ....

   ....

c your / does / Where / swimming / brother / go / ?

   ....

   ....

   sometimes / goes / He / to / club / the / .

   ....

   ....

d does / go / When / he / ?

   ....

   ....

   always / goes / on / He / Saturdays / .

   ....

   ....

5 Write the correct form of the verb *do* in these questions.

a Where ...*does*... Cristina play soccer?

b When .... Billy and Ned go swimming?

c What .... Janie do in her free time?

d Who .... they go shopping with?

6 Match the answers to the questions in Activity 5.

1 They usually go on Tuesdays.   [*b*]

2 Near her house.   ☐

3 Their parents.   ☐

4 She often watches TV.   ☐

Pronunciation: intonation in questions

7 Read these sentences. Does the intonation go up or down?

a What's your name?   up   (down)

b Do you live here?   up   down

c Where do you live?   up   down

d When do you go shopping?   up   down

e Do you like travelling?   up   down

f Does he work in a bank?   up   down

🔊 Now listen to Track 30 and check your answers.

Function: agreeing and disagreeing on statements

8 Match the questions and the answers.

1 We love playing soccer. It's fun.

2 Ronaldhino is Mexican, right?

3 You like going shopping, don't you?

4 Susie really likes doing puzzles.

a Certainly not. He's Brazilian.

b I agree. It's great fun.

c No, that's not right. She likes reading.

d Of course I do.

🔊 Listen to Track 31 and check your answers.

9 Agree or disagree with these statements.

a You like travelling, don't you?

....

b English is fun.

....

c Shakira is French, right?

....

d I like Chinese food. It's delicious.

....

🔊 Now listen to Track 32 and answer when it's your turn.

How did you do?

10 Translate these sentences into your language.

a I like doing puzzles.

....

b What do you do in your free time?

....

c We usually play basketball on Saturdays.

....

d They never watch TV.

....

e When do you go to the cinema?

....

f Of course not.

....

Phonetics

11 Look the phonemic symbols in the booklet. Write these words from Unit 7 in normal spelling.

a /ˈsʌmtaɪmz/ ....

b /ˈjuːʒəliː/ ....

c /ˈɔːlweɪz/ ....

d /əˈkeɪʒənliː/ ....

🔊 Listen to Track 33 and check your answers.

UNIT 8 How do you feel?

Grammar: frequency

1 Look at the table and ask or answer the questions.

	Mon	Tues	Weds	Thurs	Fri	Sat	Sun
Corinne	📖	📖	📖	📖	📖	📖 🏋	📖 🏋
Emma and Rich	🏋	🏋	🏋	🏋	🏋	⚽ 📺	📺
Charlie	⚽ 📺	📺	⚽ 📺	📺	⚽ 📺	📖 📺	📖 📺
Alice and Ella	📖	🏋		🏋	📺	📺	📺

a How often does Corinne read?

~~Every day.~~

b How often do Emma and Rich read?

....

c How often does Charlie play football?

.... ?

d .... ?

Twice a week.

e .... ?

Never.

f .... ?

Three times a week.

2 Put the words in the correct order to make questions and answer the questions about you.

a often / you / swimming / do / How / go / ?

~~How often do you go swimming?~~

b read / newspaper / How / you / do / often / the / ?

....

c homework / often / do / do / you / How / ?

....

Vocabulary: parts of the body

3 Unscramble these words to find parts of the body.

a yee ~~eye~~

b rea ....

c ram ....

d gel ....

e ndah ....

f toof ....

g hotot ....

h cakb ....

i hects ....

j sone ....

k cotsamh ....

l hortta ....

m uhtom ....

4 Complete this table with all the parts of the body that you need to do these things.

Eat	Play football	Use a computer	Work out	Listen to an MP3 player
mouth				

Function: asking and answering about health

5 Find three conversations here. Write them in the correct order.

He's got a problem. [ ]
I feel awful. My head hurts. [ ]
Poor Janie. [ ]
What's wrong with Billy? [ ]
Her throat hurts. [ ]
You poor thing! [ ]
How do you feel? [ ]
Oh, dear. Poor Billy. [ ]
What's the matter with Janie? [1]

a *What's the matter with Janie?*

....

....

b ....

....

c ....

....

....

Now listen to Track 34 and check your answers.

6 Listen to Track 35 and say your lines when you hear the beep.

Pronunciation: /t/ and /θ/ sounds

7 Listen to the words on Track 36. Same (S) or different (D)?

a ...... b ...... c ...... d ...... e ...... f ...... g ...... h ...... i ......

8 Listen again and write the symbol (/t/ or /θ/) you hear in the word.

a .... d .... g ....

b .... e .... h ....

c .... f .... i ....

How did you do?

9 Find the mistakes in these sentences and correct them below.

a How often does you go swimming?

....

b I go swimming four times year.

....

c Always he watches TV.

....

d Six people sometimes eats hamburgers.

....

e What's matter with you?

....

f I'm sorry hear that.

....

Phonetics

10 Look at the phonemic symbols in the booklet. Write these words from Unit 8 in normal spelling.

a /fʊt/ ....

b /θrəʊt/ ....

c /maʊθ/ ....

d /tu:θ/ ....

Listen to Track 37 and check your answers.

Review: grammar and functions

1 Put these two conversations in order. Match them to the pictures.

Oh dear. Poor Klaus.	[ ]
At half past six.	[ ]
Do you like getting up early?	[ ]
Why doesn't he have lunch?	[ ]
Oh. So what time do you get up?	[ ]
His tooth hurts when he eats.	[ ]
What's the matter with Klaus?	[1]
No, I hate it, but I start work at quarter past seven.	[ ]
Yes, I agree.	[ ]
He's hungry.	[ ]
That's awful. Getting up early is difficult.	[ ]

Conversation ....

a **A:** What's the matter with Klaus?

  B: ....

  ....

  ....

b **A:** ....

  B: ....

  ....

  ....

Conversation ....

Listen to Track 38 and check your answers.

2 Look at these charts about weekly routines. Answer the questions.

	Mon	Tues	Weds	Thurs	Fri	Sat	Sun
Linda	Work out		Work out		Work out		Lunch with parents
Patrick	Get up at 6.00	Get up at 6.00	Get up at 6.00	Get up at 6.00	Get up at 6.00	Get up at 9.00 Play soccer	Get up at 9.00
Sue and Jayne	Watch TV	WatchTV	Watch TV	Watch TV	Go to the cinema	Go shopping	

a How often does Linda work out?

  Three times a week.

b When does Patrick play soccer?

  ....

c What do Sue and Jayne do on Fridays?

  ....

d Who does Linda have lunch with on Sundays?

  ....

e How often do Sue and Jayne watch TV?

  ....

f What time does Patrick get up on Sundays?

  ....

3 Write the question.

a <u>How often does Patrick get up at 9.00</u> ?

Twice a week.

b .... ?

They go shopping.

c .... ?

She goes with Jayne.

d .... ?

Five times a week.

e .... ?

She works out.

f .... ?

He plays soccer.

Review: vocabulary

WORD LIST

arm back baseball basketball box bread
breakfast cake can carton cheese chest
chicken chocolate dinner doing puzzles ear
eye fish and chips fly foot football fruit
get up go to bed going shopping going to the
cinema golf ham hand have a shower head
hurt leg listening to music lunch meat meet
midday midnight mouth nose packet pie
playing video games problem reading relax
running salad sandwich skateboarding skiing
sleep snacks soup stomach study swimming
tennis throat tooth travelling tuna vegetables
volleyball wash watch TV work working out

4 Group words from the list into these categories:

| Related to Food |
| bread |

| Hobbies |

| Everyday activities |

| Parts of the body |

Which words are left?

Review: pronunciation

5 Find all the nouns in the word list that contain a /t/ or /θ/ sound.

/t/	/θ/
basketball	mouth

Listen to Track 39 to check your answers.

6 Listen to Track 40. Does the intonation go up or down?

a Do you get up early on Saturdays?   (up)   down

b What time do you go to bed?   up   down

c How often do you do your
homework?   up   down

d Where do you live?   up   down

e Does she live in France?   up   down

f Are they German?   up   down

Practise saying the questions with the correct pronunciation.

7 Find all the verbs in the word list. Write them in the correct column, according to their pronunciation of third person 's'.

/z/	/s/	/ɪz/
goes to bed		

Listen to Track 41 to check your answers.

Grammar: countable and uncountable nouns

1 Put these nouns in the correct column.

a pair of shoes   some chicken   three ties
a pair of trousers   two dresses   six eggs
some tea   some pens   a book

Countable	Uncountable
two dresses	

2 Complete these sentences and questions with *how much* or *how many*, *some* or *a*.

a *How much* chicken do you want?

b I want to buy .... chicken.

c I need to buy .... pair of trousers.

d .... pens do you need?

e Do you need .... eggs?

f .... eggs do you want?

g Do you need .... new dress?

h .... tea do you want?

Vocabulary: clothes

3 Write the names of these pieces of clothing in the correct place in this diagram.

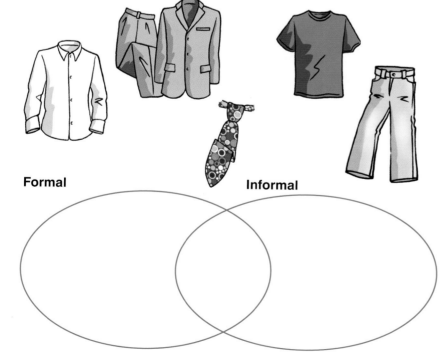

Formal   Informal

Add other clothes words you know to the diagram.

4 Complete these sentences with names of clothes.

a How much is that pair of t*rousers* ?

b I need to buy a new s .... and t .... for a wedding.

c Do you like these t .... ?

d I need a d .... for a party.

e Laura wears a s .... to work.

f John wears a s .... and t .... to work.

g On Fridays we wear T-s .... in the office.

Function: Buying things

5 Put these expressions into the correct column.

a It's £1.50 a loaf.
b £50. Do you want to try it?
c I'll take two, please. How much is that?
d I'd like a dress.
e Excuse me. How much is this bread?
f Certainly. What about this black one?
g No, thank you.
h How much does it cost?
i That's £3.00. Anything else?
j Yes, please.

Customer	Assistant
	a

6 Make two conversations.

1 *Customer: Excuse me. How much is this bread?*
....
....
....

2 ....
....
....
....

Now listen to Track 42 and check your answers.

7 Complete this conversation.

WOMAN: Excuse me. How much is that chicken?

....

WOMAN: Two kilos, please.

....

WOMAN: No, thank you.

....

Listen to Track 43 and say your lines when you hear the beep.

Pronunciation: sentence stress

8 Underline the word that has the main stress in these questions.

a How many <u>apples</u> do you want?
b How much bread do you want?
c How many eggs do you want?
d How much salad do you want?
e How much does this meat cost?
f How many bananas do you want?

Now listen to Track 44 and check your answers.

Practise saying the questions with the same stress and intonation.

How did you do?

9 Translate these sentences into your language.

a How much is that skirt?

....

b Have you got a medium?

....

c Anything else?

....

d How much does this tie cost?

....

e How many eggs do you want?

....

f I want to buy a computer.

....

Phonetics

10 Look at the phonemic symbols in the booklet. Write these words from Unit 9 in normal spelling.

a /ʃuːz/ ....
b /suːt/ ....
c /ʃɜːt/ ....
d /ˈdʒækɪt/ ....

Listen to Track 45 and check your answers.

Function: Asking for language help

1 Match the questions with the answers.

   a What does 'clothes' mean?
   b How do you say 'not very often'?
   c What does 'magazine' mean?
   d How do you say 'the part of your body where food goes'?

   1 Occasionally
   2 Stomach
   3 Things we wear
   4 It's something to read and it has a lot of pictures.

Now listen to Track 46 and check your answers.

2 Put the words in order to make a conversation.

   a want / you / to / come / Do / cinema / us / the / with / to / ?
   Do you want to come to the cinema with us?

   b speak / please / Can / slowly / you / ? / more

   c great / this / There's / movie / evening / a / .

   d 'movie' / mean / does / What / ?

   e film / a / It's / .

   f that / say / you / Can / please / again / ?

   g cinema / is / movie / A / the / at / a / film / .

   h love / movie / go / I'd / the / to / to / !

Now listen to Track 47 and check your answer.

3 Now listen to Track 48 and say your lines when you hear the beep.

Vocabulary: actions

4 Complete these sentences with the correct verb below:

   ~~drive~~ ◆ ride ◆ jump ◆ hit ◆ clap
   dance ◆ clap ◆ cheer ◆ fall

   a I usually ...*drive*... my car to work.

   b People always .... at the theatre.

   c In volleyball you .... the ball.

   d When people watch sports they often ....

   e If people run fast, they sometimes ....

5 Match the person to the picture. Then write what these people do, using one of the verbs from Activity 4.

   a a bus driver   pic ....
   A bus driver drives buses.

   b a mountain climber pic ....

   c a ballet dancer   pic ....

   d a baseball player   pic ....

   e a horse rider   pic ....

   f a spectator   pic ....

Grammar: present continuous

6 Write the correct form of the verb *be* in these sentences.

a What ......is.... Jake doing?

b .... she singing?

c .... Susie and John going home?

d Where .... Lucy going?

e We .... watching TV.

f Maria .... not coming to the party.

7 Look at this picture and write what the people are doing.

a Hank is throwing the ball. ....

b ....

c ....

d ....

e ....

f ....

Pronunciation: /n/ and /ŋ/

8 Listen to Track 49 and identify whether the words a-f end in the sound /n/ (thin) or /ŋ/ (thing).

/n/ or /ŋ/	word		/n/ or /ŋ/	word
a /ʌ/	thin	e	....	....
b	....	f	....	....
c	....	g	....	....
d	....			

9 Listen again and write the word on the line. Practise saying the words.

How did you do?

10 Find the mistakes in these sentences and correct them below.

a What does 'movie' means?

....

b I usually drive my bicycle to school.

....

c We watching TV at the moment.

....

d John not going home.

....

e She's wear a red dress today.

....

f They's having fun.

....

Phonetics

11 Look at the phonemic symbols in the booklet. Write these words from Unit 10 in normal spelling.

a /sɪŋ/............................

b /ˈgəʊɪŋ/............................

c /θɪŋk/............................

d /ˈθɪŋkɪŋ/............................

Listen to Track 50 and check your answers.

UNIT 11 Fashion

Vocabulary: Describing hair, body and face

Helen

Frank

Larry

Alicia

1 Read these sentences and write the name of the person.

a He is short and a bit chubby. He's got long blonde hair and blue eyes. ....

b She is tall and she is a bit overweight. She has long dark hair and dark eyes. ....

2 Write sentences about the other two people.

....

....

....

....

....

....

Function: describing people

3 The five statements/questions in 1–5 should be followed by a question a–e. Put them in the correct order.

1 Do you know Joe?
2 He's got short blond hair and blue eyes.
3 About 1.85, I think.
4 I don't know. He's slim, maybe about 90 kilos.
5 About 25.

a I think I know him. How old is he?
b Is he thin? How much does he weigh?
c Oh, yes, I know him. What about him?
d Hmm. How tall is he?
e I'm not sure. What does he look like?

))) Listen to Track 51 to check your answers.

4 Complete this conversation about Maxine.

DRIVER LICENSE
D01234567

MAXINE SANDERS
AGE: 21
HEIGHT: 5'5"
WEIGHT: 125 LBS
EYES: BROWN
HAIR: BLACK

YOU: _Do you know Maxine?_

MAN: I'm not sure. What does she look like?

YOU: ....

MAN: Hmm. How tall is she?

YOU: ....

MAN: How much does she weigh?

YOU: ....

MAN: Yes, I think I know her. How old is she?

YOU: ....

))) Now listen to Track 52 and say your lines when you hear the beep.

Grammar: present continuous (*wh-* questions)

HEATHER

JED MARLA CHRIS

NICOLE

5 Look at the picture and answer the questions.

a What is Heather doing?

She's walking on the catwalk.

b What is Nicole wearing?

....

c Who is Jed eating with?

....

d What is Chris wearing?

....

6 Look at the picture again and write the questions that go with these answers.

a *Who is Marla eating with* .... ?

With Jed.

b .... ?

A black dress and grey shoes.

c .... ?

She's talking on her mobile phone.

d .... ?

She's wearing a white T-shirt and black trousers and he's wearing a white T-shirt and jeans.

Pronunciation: contractions of verb *be*

7 Listen to Track 53 and circle what you hear.

a Yes, I am/I'm watching the television.

b You are/You're talking too much.

c She is/'s climbing the tree.

d No, he isn't/is not coming home for dinner.

e Yes, they are/they're singing.

f Yes, we are/we're coming to your party.

8 Listen to Track 53 again and practise saying the sentences with the same pronunciation.

How did you do?

9 Translate these sentences into your language.

a He's got short dark hair.

....

b What does she look like?

....

c Where are you phoning from?

....

d Who are you having lunch with?

....

Phonetics

10 Look at the phonemic symbols in the booklet. Write these words from Unit 11 in normal spelling.

a /ʃɔːt/..

b /lɒŋ/..

c /θɪn/..

d /tɔːl/..

Listen to Track 54 and check your answers.

UNIT 12 In contact

Vocabulary: interacting

1 Complete these sentences with a verb. Some words may be used more than once.

send ◆ go ◆ take ◆ leave ◆ play ◆ make

a I often ___leave___ messages on Jane's answering machine.

b Do you want to _____ a video game on the computer?

c I need to _____ a call on my mobile phone.

d Why don't you _____ a text message?

e You can find his address if you _____ online.

f I'm going to _____ photographs with my new digital camera.

g She has a fax machine, so you can _____ her a fax.

2 Describe what people are doing in this picture.

Ron is making a phone call.

_____

_____

_____

_____

Grammar: present continuous and present simple

3 Complete these sentences with the present simple or present continuous tense.

a I usually work in an office, but today I _'m working_ (work) at home.

b At the moment I'm watching TV, but I never _____ (watch) TV in the morning.

c Jake often writes emails, but today _____ (make) phone calls.

d Sally _____ (not speak) French, but she _____ (take) classes at the moment.

e Jack and Jenny _____ (not take) photos very often, but today they're using their mobile phone to take pictures.

f Margarita _____ (live) in Spain at the moment, but she usually _____ (live) in Peru.

4 Write phrases from Activity 4 in the correct column.

Habits, things we do regularly	Facts about things and people	Happening at this very moment, now, as we speak	Happening now (this week, this year, etc.)
Jake often writes emails.			

Function: using the telephone

5 Complete this dialogue.

MARIANA: Hello?

FERNANDO: Hello. ....

MARIANA: Can I ....
    Lyndsay, please?

FERNANDO: She's not here.

.... ?

MARIANA: .... Mariana.

FERNANDO: Do you want to

.... ?

MARIANA: Yes, please. Can you
    tell her that Mariana and
    Robin aren't coming to the
    party, because Robin is sick.

FERNANDO: Sure, I'll tell her.

MARIANA: ....

....

FERNANDO: ....

Listen to Track 55 and check
your answers.

6 Now listen to Track 56 and
answer as Fernando.

7 Complete this form about the
message.

MESSAGES

Message for:
_____

Message taken by:
_____

Message:
_____

_____

_____

_____

Returned your call ☐
Please call ☐
Will call you ☐

Pronunciation: /ʌ/ and /ɒ/

8 Listen to Track 57 and circle which word you hear.

a boss / bus
b boss / bus
c hot / hut
d hot / hut
e cop / cup
f cop / cup
g song / sung
h song / sung

9 Listen again and write the phonemic symbol of the word you hear.

a ....
b ....
c ....
d ....
e ....
f ....
g ....
h ....

Practise saying the words with the correct pronunciation.

How did you do?

10 Find the mistakes in these sentences and correct them.

a I always send reports on fax. ....
b I'm usually living in London. ....
c She's never having important meetings. ....
d Do you want leave a message? ....
e Who's speaking? I'm Joe. ....
f Can I taking a message? ....

Phonetics

11 Look at the phonemic symbols in the booklet. Write these words from Unit 12 in normal spelling.

a /lʌv/ ....
b /mʌniː/ ....
c /dʌz/ ....
d /bɒs/ ....

Listen to Track 58 and check your answers.

Review Units 9–12

Review: grammar and functions

1 Listen to Track 59. Which person is Candy? A, B or C?

 A  B  C

2 Write a description of one of the other two women.

_____

_____

3 Match the question to the answer.

a How tall is he?
b What's Jake doing?
c Can I speak to Mike, please?
d How much is that skirt?
e Are Jane and Susie watching TV?
f How much do they cost?
g What does 'climb' mean?
h How many do you want?
i How do you say 'go up' a tree?
j Do you want to try it?

1 Sure, he's right here.
2 No, they aren't.
3 He's washing his car.
4 Climb.
5 When you go up.
6 Three, please.
7 1 metre 90.
8 $25.
9 $5 each.
10 Yes, please.

4 Ask and answer questions about this food.

> milk at only 50p a litre

> **1lb cheese for £4**

> eggs at only £1 per dozen

> salad at £1.50 a bag

a Ask and answer about price

1 Q: How much is that cheese? A: _____

2 _____

3 _____

4 _____

b Ask about quantity

1 Q: How much cheese do you want? _____

2 _____

3 _____

4 _____

5 Now complete these dialogues.

a WOMAN: Hello. I'd like
_____some cheese_____, please.

ASSISTANT: Certainly, how
_____ do you want?

WOMAN: How _____ ?

ASSISTANT: £5.50 a pound.

WOMAN: I'll take half a pound please.

ASSISTANT: Here you are. That's £2.25, please.

WOMAN: Thanks.

b MAN: I need _____ .

ASSISTANT: How _____

_____ ?

MAN: Just a dozen, please.

ASSISTANT: OK. Anything else?

MAN: No, thanks. How

_____ ?

ASSISTANT: £1.50, please.

MAN: There you are.

ASSISTANT: Thanks.

Review: vocabulary

WORD LIST

answering machine   article   birthday present
blond   carnival   CD   CD player   cheer   chubby
clap   climb   club   contact   cost   costumes   curly
dance   dress   drive   fall   fat   fax machine   fun
go on the Internet   having fun   hit   how many ...?
how much ...?   in contact   interacting   jacket
jump   leave a voice message   long   look like
magazine   make a phone call   medium build
medium height   medium length   meeting
mobile phone   MP3 player   organise   overweight
pair   ride   send a fax   send a text message
send an email   shirt   shoes   short   sing   skirt
slim   sock   straight   suit   sweater   take
photographs   tall   thin   throw   tie   trousers
T-shirt

6 Group words from the list into these categories:

Describing people and what they wear

Verbs and activities

Related to technology
fax machine

Others

Review: pronounciation

7 Find all the adjectives and nouns in the word list that contain a /ʌ/ or /ɒ/ sound.

/ʌ/	/ɒ/
chubby	

Listen to Track 60 to check your answers.

8 Listen to Track 61. Underline the stressed word.

a How much is that <u>shirt</u>?
b Can you speak slowly, please?
c She's got dark brown hair.
d He's got light blue eyes.
e Can I take a message?
f How much does it cost?

Practise saying the questions with the correct pronunciation.

9 Find all the words in the word list that have the sound /n/ or /ŋ/.

/n/	/ŋ/
machine	

Listen to Track 62 to check your answers.

Vocabulary: rooms and furniture

1 Find these words in this word search.

> TV ◆ bed ◆ sofa ◆ chair ◆ curtains ◆ rug ◆ desk ◆ stove ◆ shower
> toilet ◆ lamp ◆ computer ◆ table ◆ fridge

```
S O F A C B E G D I R F
T S G H I O K J E F E R
O W Y I U N H Y S Q W K
V D T Z X P B N K M O E
E W A Y G I P M F V H C
D B B C U R T A I N S M
Q R L I R P L D L A M P
H J E K M N B R S E T U
K O P L T E L I O T E P
S Y B E D W B A M N K B
X P A H M L U H Y T R S
R E T U P M O C I V Q D
```

2 Write the words from Activity 1 in the correct column.

living room
kitchen
bedroom *bed*
bathroom
dining room

Grammar: possessions; prepositions

3 What is the meaning of *'s* in the sentences a – d?
Write P (possession) or *Be* (abbreviation of *is*).

a Scott's five friends ....P....

b Jenny's teacher ....

c Jenny's a teacher ....

d Scott's five ....

Write a – d as captions under the pictures.

1 ....

2 ....

3 ....

4 ....

4 Find the mistakes in these sentences and correct them below.

a What's his wife's name? Her name's is Jane.

....

b How old is your daughter? My daughter's is twenty.

....

c What does your son do? He's student.

....

d What colour is Jimmy's car? He's car blue.

....

e Is James a doctor? No, he's is a dentist.

....

f What's your brother name? His name Rafael.

....

5 Look at the picture and complete the sentences about Jane and Martin's possessions.

a Jane's shoes are *under the bed* .

b .... next to the desk.

c .... is opposite the door.

d Martin's book ....

e Jane's lamp is .... the bed

and ....

f .... on ....

g Martin and Jane's computer ....

near ....

Pronunciation: plurals

6 Listen to Track 63 and write the symbol of the plural pronunciation that you hear. /s/ /z/ or /ɪz/.

a .... **f** ....

b .... **g** ....

c .... **h** ....

d .... **i** ....

e ....

Practise saying the words with the correct pronunciation.

Function: looking for something

7 Find two conversations here.

Oh, yes. Here it is.	[ ]
In the living room.	[ ]
Where's the newspaper?	[ ]
Are they in the living room?	[ ]
Where are my glasses?	[ ]
No, it isn't under the newspaper.	[ ]
Have you seen my watch?	[1]
Oh, yes, here they are next to the TV.	[ ]
Are they on the fridge?	[ ]
Is it in the bathroom?	[ ]
No, they aren't in the kitchen.	[ ]
No. Is it under the newspaper?	[ ]

Conversation 1

Man: *Have you seen my watch?* ....

Woman: ....

....

....

....

....

Conversation 2

Woman: ....

Man: ....

....

....

....

Listen to Track 64 and check your answers.

8 Write a conversation in this situation.

KENNY: Have you seen ...my keys?...

MARIE: No. .... ?

KENNY: No, they aren't.

MARIE: .... ?

KENNY: No.

MARIE: .... ?

KENNY: Oh, yes. Here they are. Thanks.

9 Listen to Track 65 and say your lines when you hear the beep.

10 Translate these sentences into your language.

a The sofa is in the living room.

....

b Bobby's eight years old.

....

c Bobby's daughter's eight years old.

....

d The pen is next to the computer.

....

e Have you seen my keys?

....

f Where are my glasses?

....

Phonetics

11 Look at the phonemic symbols in the booklet. Write these words from Unit 13 in normal spelling.

a /'bedru:mz/ ....

b /'desks/ ....

c /'wɒtʃɪz/ ....

d /'læmps/ ....

e /'frɪdʒɪz/ ....

f /'kɪtʃənz/ ....

Listen to Track 66 and check your answers.

UNIT 14 Finding things

Vocabulary: public places

1 Do this crossword puzzle.

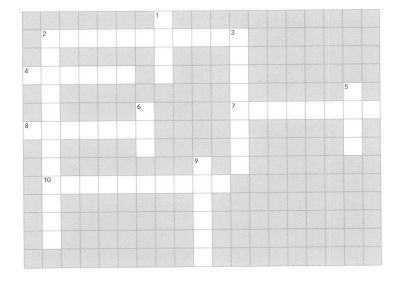

Across
2 Buy your groceries here
4 See a movie here
7 If your stomach hurts, go here
8 Take out a book to read here
10 Get a stamp here

Down
1 Go for a walk here
2 Go swimming here
3 Do business here
5 Get some money here
6 Work out here
9 Children learn here

Function: asking for and giving directions

2 Look at the map and complete the conversation.

MAN: Excuse me, _is there_ a hospital near here?
WOMAN: Yes, dear. .... this street. Turn .... onto Green St and .... the street. The hospital is ....

🔊 Listen to Track 67 and check your answers.

3 Write directions for these places.

a Excuse me. Where's the library?

Walk along Park Street. The library is on your right.
....

b Excuse me. Is there a supermarket near here? ....
....

c Excuse me. Where's the cinema? ....
....

d Excuse me. Where's the town hall? ....
....

4 Now listen to Track 68 and answer when you hear the beep.

Grammar: *there is/there are*

5 Look at the picture and complete these sentences about what you see.

a <u>There is a</u> tomato.

b .... milk.

c .... eggs.

d .... apples.

e .... chicken.

f .... door.

6 Complete these questions and answer them.

a .... juice? ....

b .... grapes? ....

c .... pineapple? ....

Pronunciation: /r/

7 Listen to these conversations and underline the sound /r/ when it is pronounced.

a Is the<u>re a</u> hospital in this town?
   Yes, there is. It's near the car park.

b Are there any supermarkets near here?
   Yes, there are. There are two.

c Where is the town hall?
   There isn't a town hall here.

Listen to Track 69 and check your answers.

8 Practise saying the conversations with the same pronunciation.

How did you do?

9 Find the mistakes in these sentences and correct them below.

a Are there a bank near here?

....

b There is some table in the dining room.

....

c There aren't any milk.

....

d Is there any rugs in your house?

....

e In our town there is three supermarkets.

....

f There isn't no computer in our house.

....

Phonetics

10 Look at the phonemic symbols in the booklet. Write these words from Unit 14 in normal spelling.

a /'suːpəmɑkət/..

b /'kɑː pɑːk/..

c /'ʃɒpɪŋ sentə/..

d /'spɔːts sentə/..

Listen to Track 70 and check your answers.

Can you play the piano?

Vocabulary: music

1 Complete these ads with the names of musical instruments and types of music.

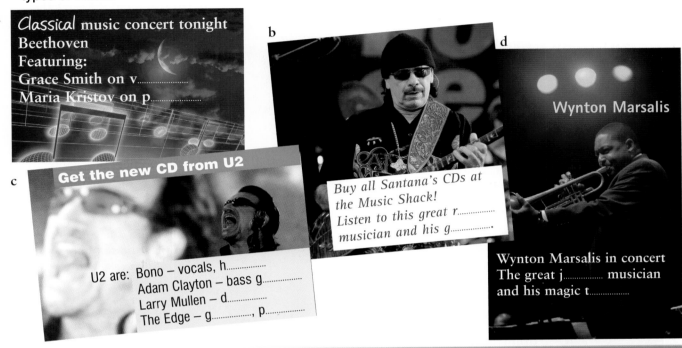

a
Classical music concert tonight
Beethoven
Featuring:
Grace Smith on v........
Maria Kristov on p........

b

d
Wynton Marsalis

c
Get the new CD from U2

Buy all Santana's CDs at the Music Shack!
Listen to this great r............ musician and his g............ .

U2 are: Bono – vocals, h............
Adam Clayton – bass g............
Larry Mullen – d............
The Edge – g............ , p............

Wynton Marsalis in concert
The great j............ musician and his magic t............

2 Put the words in the right order to make questions.

a turn / down / mMay / the / I / music / ?
May I turn the music down?

b window / mind / you / open / Do / I / the / if / ?

....

c go / I/ party / Can / tonight / Joe's / to / ?

....

d the / mind / Do / watch / TV / you / I / if / ?

....

e car / borrow / your/ I / can / ?

....

f your / listen / Can / to / CDs / I /?

....

3 Now match questions a – f with the answers.

___b___ No, I don't. Go ahead.

.... Sure. Find something you like.

.... OK, but I need it this afternoon.

.... Yes, of course. It's very loud.

.... That's fine. See if there's a good programme.

.... No, you can't. You have school tomorrow.

Listen to Track 71 and check your answers.

4 Now listen to Track 72 and say your lines when you hear the beep.

Grammar: *can / can't*

5 Read this paragraph about Stevie Wonder and complete the table about him.

Stevie Wonder is one of the most famous musicians of all time, and what is most interesting is that he can't see – Steveland Morris (his real name) is totally blind. Stevie is an amazing musician: he can play the keyboards (piano and synthesizer), the drums, the bass guitar and the harmonica, but he can't play the trumpet, the cello or the violin.

Stevie Wonder	can	can't
	play keyboards	....
	....	....
	....	....

6 Look at this information about Paul McCartney and write a paragraph about him.

	can	can't
	play keyboards, guitar	trumpet, saxophone
	drums	violin

....

....

....

....

Pronunciation: /kɑːnt/ /kæn/ /kən/

7 Listen to these conversations on Track 73 and write the symbol of the pronunciation of *can/can't* that you hear.

a A: Can ...*kæn*... you play the guitar?

B: Yes, I can ....

b A: Can .... you play the trumpet?

B: No, I can't .... , but I can .... play the violin.

c A: Can .... you read music?

B: No, I can't .... , but I can .... sing.

◁)) Listen to Track 73 and check your answers.

8 Practise saying the conversations with the same pronunciation.

How did you do?

9 Translate these sentences into your language.

a Can I go to a party tonight?

....

....

b Do you mind if I leave the room?

....

....

c May I turn the TV off?

....

....

d Can you play the piano?

....

....

e I can't play the trumpet, but I can play the saxophone.

....

....

f She can play the guitar and she can sing.

....

....

Phonetics

10 Look at the phonemic symbols in the booklet. Write these words from Unit 15 in normal spelling.

a /kən juː ˈsɪŋ/............

b /jes, aɪ ˈkæn/............

c /nəʊ, aɪ kɑːnt/............

d /ʃi kɑːnt ˈsi/............

◁)) Listen to Track 74 and check your answers.

Grammar: *must* and *have to*

1 Look at these rules and write them in the correct column.

Rules for Art class
You **must** clean up after class.
You **mustn't** eat during class.
You **don't have to** be silent during class.
You **don't have to** stay in your seat.
You **mustn't** touch other people's work.
You **mustn't** work on other subjects during art class.
You **mustn't** run in the art classroom.
You **must** stay until the bell rings.
You **must** ask for permission to leave the classroom.

Yes	No	Not necessary
clean up after class		

2 Now complete these questions and answer them.

a ......Do...... you have to clean up after class?
....

b Do .... stay in your seat?
....

c .... to stay until the bell rings?
....

d .... you ask permission to leave the classroom? ....

e .... you be silent during class?
....

Vocabulary: studying

3 Name the subject.

a ....

b ....

c ....

d ....

e ....

f ....

g ....

$E=MC^2$

h ....

4 Write the subjects in the right place in this diagram.

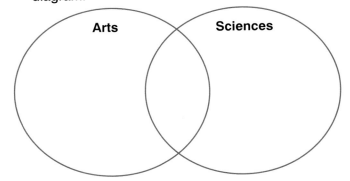

Arts   Sciences

Pronunciation: *have to* and *don't have to*

5 Listen to Track 75 and put the sentences that you hear in order.

 a I have to wait in the gym. ....**1**....

   I have two weights in the gym. ....**2**....

 b They don't have to play in the theatre. ....

   They don't have two plays in the theatre. ....

 c She has to work in the museum. ....

   She has two works in the museum. ....

   Underline the stressed words.

6 Practise saying the sentences with the same stress and pronunciation.

Function: lending and borrowing

7 Read these sentences and choose the correct form.

 a Can you <u>lend</u> / borrow me a book?
 b Can I lend / borrow a pencil?
 c Can I lend / borrow your car?
 d Can you lend / borrow me a jacket?

8 Now match them with the correct answer.

 1 ....**c**.... Sorry. I have to drive my grandmother to the shops.

 2 .... Sure. I have a sweater I can wear.

 3 .... OK. This one is great – it's a really interesting story.

 4 .... Sorry. I only have one and I'm using it.

 Now listen to Track 76 and check your answers.

9 Listen to Track 77 and say your lines when you hear the beep.

How did you do?

10 Find the mistakes in these sentences and correct them below.

 a You must to study hard.

 ....

 b We don't has to go to every class.

 ....

 c They haven't to do any homework.

 ....

 d Do you must speak French at work?

 ....

 e Can you borrow me some money?

 ....

 f Can I lend your MP3 player?

 ....

Phonetics

11 Look at the phonemic symbols in the booklet. Write these words from Unit 16 in normal spelling.

 a /ˈfɪzɪks/...

 b /ˈkemɪstriː/...

 c /baɪˈɒlədʒiː/..

 d /mæθs/...

 e /ˈdʒɪɒɡrəfiː/..

 f /ˈhɪstriː/...

 Listen to Track 78 and check your answers.

Review: grammar and functions

1 Look at the pictures and complete the dialogues.

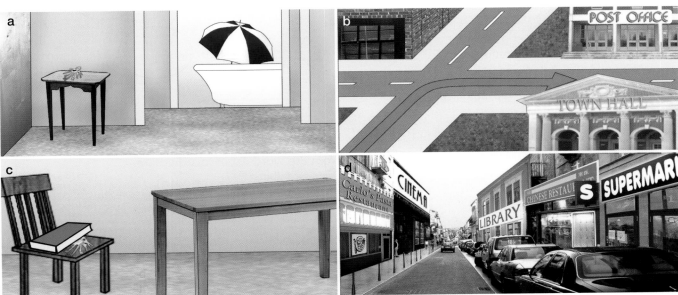

a

JODY: Mark! Have you seen my _umbrella_ ?

MARK: I think it's .... the door.

JODY: No, my keys are there, but I .... find my ....

MARK: Is it in the .... ?

JODY: Oh yes, that's right. Thanks.

b

FRANK: Excuse me. Is there a .... near here?

MARTHA: Hmmm. Yes, there is. Go straight down this street, then turn .... and the .... is on the left, ... the town hall.

FRANK: Thanks.

c

SUZANNA: Where are my .... ?

JAMES: They're on the table.

SUZANNA: No, they aren't.

JAMES: Are they .... that book?

SUZANNA: Oh yes, thanks. They're .... the chair.

d

OLD LADY: Excuse me. Are there any .... near here?

YOUNG MAN: Yes, there .... two. There's one next to the cinema on the .... and there's one .... the supermarket and the library on the right.

OLD LADY: Thank you.

Now listen to Track 79 and check your answers.

2 Match the question to the answer.

a Do I have to go to every class?
b Can I go to Jane's party?
c May I leave the table?
d Do you mind if I turn the music up?
e Can I borrow your phone?
f Can you lend me some money?
g Is there a park near here?
h Are there any rugs in your house?
i Can you speak French?

1 Sure. It's very quiet.
2 OK. We've finished dinner.
3 No, you can't. You have school tomorrow.
4 Yes, you do.
5 No. There aren't any parks around here.
6 Certainly. How much do you need?
7 No, I can't.
8 Yes, we have two in the living room.
9 Sorry. I need it.

Review: vocabulary

and   Art   bank   bar   bass guitar
bathroom   bed   bedroom
between   bicycle   Biology   bridge
but   car park   chair   Chemistry
clarinet   classical music   club
computer   country music   curtains
dance music   desk   dining room
drums   English   fridge   Geography
guitar   gym   harmonica   hip-hop
History   hospital   in   jazz
keyboard(s)   kitchen   lamp   library
living room   Mathematics (Maths)
museum   near   next to   on
opposite   park   Physical Education (PE)
Physics   piano   pop music
post office   restaurant   rug
saxophone   school   shopping centre
shower   sofa   stamp   supermarket
swimming pool   table   toilet
town hall   trumpet   TV   umbrella
under   violin

3   Write words from the word list into this diagram.

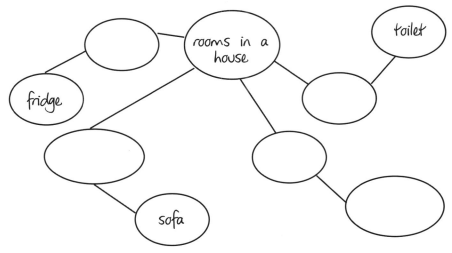

4   Write words from the word list in this diagram.

Types of music	jazz				
Typical instruments used					

Review: pronunciation

5   Find all the countable nouns in the word list and put them in the correct column, according to the pronunciation of their plurals.

/s/	/z/	/ɪz/
banks		post office

◁))) Listen to Track 80 to check your answers.

6   Which words from the word list have the sound /r/?
     bathroom
     ....
     ....

◁))) Listen to Track 81 to check your answers.

UNIT 17 Animals

Vocabulary: animals

1 Find the names of animals in this puzzle.

agiraffelimousehorabbitacattiregdogandrhinocerostratankangaroothehorseselephantus

2 Complete these sentences with the name of an animal.

a A __lion__ is often called the king of the jungle.

b .... only live in Australia.

c .... and .... are very common pets.

d .... like eating carrots.

e There are African and Indian ....

f A .... has a very long neck.

Function: warnings

3 Complete the warnings for these pictures. Match the warning to the picture.

KEEP OFF THE GRASS

a

b

c

d

1 __Don't__ touch that! ..... __a__

2 .... off the grass! .....

3 .... out! There's a mouse under the table. .....

4 .... the dog! .....

Now listen to Track 82 and check your answers.

4 Write one different way to give each warning.

a _Look out! It's fragile._
....

b ....
....

c ....
....

d ....
....

5 Listen to Track 83 and when you hear each warning, say it in a different way.

Pronunciation: /aɪ/ and /aʊ/

6 Same or different?

Listen to Track 84 and write S (same) or D (different) according to the words you hear.

a _S_   b ....   c ....

d ....   e ....   f ....

7 Now write the phonetic symbol for the vowel sound you hear.

a ....

b ....

c ....

d ....

e ....

f ....

Practise saying the words with the correct pronunciation.

Grammar: *imperatives*

8 Read these instructions for looking after aquarium fish. Change the instructions using imperatives.

The first thing to remember is that you must buy a fish tank that is not too big and not too small.

a _Buy a fish tank that is not too big or too small._

You must give the fish enough water.

b ....

You must change the water every week and you have to be careful to keep the water clean.

c ....

Make sure that you do not put anything in the water.

d ....

Fish need to have plants in the water to provide shelter.

e ....

The aquarium must not be in direct sunlight, because this is too hot for the fish.

f ....

You must feed the fish every day, but be careful not to give the fish too much food.

g ....

How did you do?

9 Translate these sentences into your language.

a Don't use flash photography. ....

b Stay very quiet. ....

c Mind the chewing gum! ....

d Look out for that dog! ....

e Don't forget to feed the fish. ....

f Don't let the dog out. ....

Phonetics

10 Look at the phonemic symbols in the booklet. Write these words from Unit 17 in normal spelling.

a /maʊs/ ....

b /ˈraɪnəʊ/ ....

c /ˈpeŋgwɪn/ ....

d /waɪld ˈænɪməl/ ....

e /bi ˈkeəfʊl/ ....

f /lʊk ˈaʊt/ ....

Listen to Track 85 and check your answers.

UNIT 18 Weather

Vocabulary: weather and seasons

1 **What's the weather like in these pictures?**

a It's windy and it's raining.

b ....

c ....

2 **Do this crossword.**

1 When is the weather usually hot?
2 When do flowers start to grow?
3 When is it often cold?
4 When do the leaves fall from the trees?

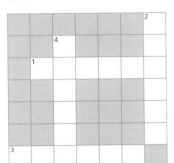

Grammar: past simple of verb *be*

3 **Read the dialogues. Match the dialogue to the picture.**

Conversation 1 Picture ....
MINA: Hi John!
JOHN: Hi Mina!
MINA: Where are you?
JOHN: We're at home.
MINA: Where were you this afternoon?
JOHN: We were at the zoo.
MINA: Oh.

Conversation 2 Picture ....
FRED: Hi Louise!
LOUISE: Hello Fred.
FRED: Where are you?
LOUISE: I'm at the zoo with Matt.
FRED: Where were you this morning?
LOUISE: At home. Why?

a   b

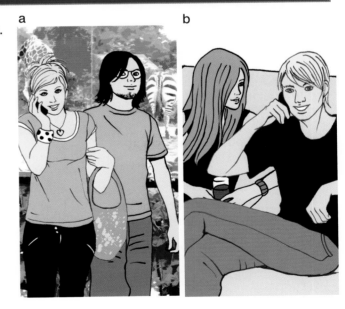

Answer these questions.

a Where is John now? .... At home. ....

b Where are Louise and Matt now? ....

c Was John at home in the afternoon? ....

d Were Matt and Louise at the zoo in the morning? ....

4 Look at the pictures and complete these questions and answers about Louise's day.

a Where ....was.... Louise this morning at 8.00 am?

She .... in bed.

b .... Louise in the gym at 7.00 pm?

Yes, ...

c .... Louise and Frankie at the office at lunch time?

No, ... They ....

d .... ?

She .... in the office.

e Where .... now?

She .... at home.

What .... ?

She ....

Function: expressing approval and disapproval

5 Match the two parts of the conversation.

a Do you like snow?
b Do you like cloudy weather?
c I love the sunshine.
d I love the rain.

1 Yes, it's lovely.
2 I don't. I hate hot weather.
3 Oh really? I don't. It's awful.
4 No, I hate cold weather.

Now listen to Track 86 and check your answers.

6 Complete this conversation. Agree or disagree.

I love watching TV. It's great!

a ....

Oh really? What about sports? Do you like sports?

b ....

That's interesting. Do you want to go out in the rain? Do you like the rain?

c ....

OK. What about hot weather? Do you like it?

d ....

Now listen to Track 87 and answer when you hear the beep.

Pronunciation: intonation

7 Listen to Track 88. Decide whether these people are happy (H) or sad (S).

a .... b .... c .... d .... e .... f ....

8 Can you guess what they are saying?

Listen to Track 89 and check your answers.

How did you do?

9 Find the mistakes in these sentences and correct them below.

a How's the weather like? ....

b Yesterday I'm at home all day. ....

c Where are you this morning at 7 o'clock? ....

d I love shopping. It's awful! ....

Phonetics

10 Look at the phonemic symbols in the booklet. Write these words from Unit 18 in normal spelling.

a /ˈterɪbəl/ ....
b /ˈɔːfʊl/ ....
c /ˈlʌvliː/ ....
d /sʌniː/ ....
e /ˈreɪnɪŋ/ ....
f /ˈklaʊdiː/ ....

Listen to Track 90 and check your answers.

UNIT 19 That's history

Vocabulary: dates and historical events

1 Write the dates.

a 1914 _nineteen fourteen_

b 1945 ....

c 1947 ....

d 1952 ....

e 1963 ....

2 Fill in the blanks with words from the box and the dates in Activity 1.

President ◆ queen ◆ World
Prime Minister ◆ War

a Elizabeth II became ___queen___ of the United Kingdom and Northern Ireland in ....

b Nehru became the first .... of independent India in ....

c World .... I started in ....

d .... War II ended in ....

e .... is the year of the assassination of .... John F. Kennedy.

Grammar: past simple (affirmative and negative)

3 Fill in the blanks in the biography with the past simple form of the verbs in brackets. Look at the list of irregular verbs in the booklet for help.

Gama, Vasco da Born 1460 in Portugal. Died 1524.

Vasco da Gama **a** ......_was_...... (*be* irreg.) the first European to go to India by sea.

He **b** .... (*leave*, irreg.) Portugal in 1497 with four small ships and 170 men. He sailed into the Atlantic and **c** .... (*turn* reg.) east to go round the Cape of Good Hope, at the tip of Africa. It **d** .... (*not be* irreg.) easy but Da Gama **e** .... (*continue* reg.) on his voyage.

After three months, the Portuguese reached the coast north of the Cape and sailed along the coast. They **f** .... (*find* irreg.) Arab towns on the coast of what is now Mozambique. Da Gama **g** .... (*become* irreg.) a friend of the Sultan of Malindi. The Sultan **h** .... (*give* irreg.) him two Arab pilots to guide him to India.

Da Gama sailed across the Indian Ocean to Calicut. There, he **i** .... (*start* reg.) to trade with the ruler, Zamorin. In 1501, he **j** .... (*arrive* reg.) back in Portugal with ships full of spices.

Da Gama **k** .... (*become* irreg.) viceroy of India in 1524. He **l** .... (*die* reg.) in India on 24th December that year.

4 These sentences are all false. Rewrite them to make them true.

a Vasco da Gama left Portugal in 1597.

He didn't leave in 1597. He left in 1497.

b He took 200 men with him.

....

c He turned west to go round the Cape of Good Hope.

....

d He reached the coast north of the Cape after three years.

....

e The Sultan of Malindi gave him two Arab ships to go to India.

....

f Vasco da Gama died in Portugal.

....

Pronunciation: *-ed* endings

5 Read the groups of verbs aloud. Cross out the verb with a different pronunciation of *-ed*.

a played   turned   lived   ~~liked~~
b kissed   cooked   died   watched
c wanted   beheaded   washed   decided
d arrived   reached   loved   divorced
e landed   ended   lifted   happened
f started   worked   baked   walked

🔊 Listen to Track 91 to check your answers.

6 Write the verbs in Activity 5 in the table according to the sound of the *-ed* ending.

/d/	/t/	/ɪd/
played	liked	wanted

🔊 Listen to Track 92 to check your answers.

Function: sequence markers

7 Work out the order of the pictures. Write *first*, *then*, *next*, *finally* and *after that* in the spaces. Use the sentences in the correct order in the text about Yuri Gagarin in Activity 8.

pic ....

Yuri flew around the Earth.

pic ....
First

He worked in a steel factory.

pic ....

He trained to become a cosmonaut.

pic ....

He became a pilot in the Russian air force.

pic ....

Yuri took flying lessons as a hobby.

8 Write the story of Yuri Gagarin's career.

Yuri Gagarin was from Russia. He was the world's first
cosmonaut. These are some important events in his life.
First,

The flight took only 1 hour and 48 minutes. Yuri Gagarin
died in 1968 when his plane crashed.

9 Talk to a friend about Yuri Gagarin.

YOUR FRIEND: Who was Yuri Gagarin?

YOU: He was the world's first cosmonaut.

YOUR FRIEND: What do you know about his career?

YOU: Well,

YOUR FRIEND: Wow! What happened after that? Did he go round
the Earth again?

YOU:

YOUR FRIEND: Oh no! That's sad.

Listen to Track 93. Say your lines after the beep.

How did you do?

10 Translate these sentences into your language.

a I saw the film but I didn't like it.

b The king died and his daughter became queen after the war.

c First he married one woman. Then he divorced her and married
another woman.

d What happened next?

e Elizabeth I didn't pay the soldiers after the war against the
Spanish Armada.

Phonetics

11 Look at the phonemic symbols
in the booklet. Write these words
from Unit 19 in normal spelling.

a /wɔː/

b /səʊldʒə/

c /ɪndɪˈpendəns/

d /muːn/

e /ˈfaɪnəlɪ/

f /bəˈnaːnə/

Listen to Track 94 to check your
answers.

Function: ending a conversations

1 Put the sentences in the right order to make a conversation.

  a Well, I have to go. It was nice to talk to you. [ ]
  b Hi! How's it going?   [**1**]
  c You too. See you around.   [ ]
  d Fine thanks. You?   [ ]
  e Great. Did you have a good holiday? [ ]
  f Yes, bye.   [ ]
  g Yes, we did. It was fun.   [ ]

Listen to Track 95 to check your answers.

2 Follow the instructions to complete the dialogue.

Greet your friend.

  a YOU: *Hi! How's it going?* ?

    YOUR FRIEND: Fine, thanks.

Ask about your friend's family.

  b YOU: _____ ?

    YOUR FRIEND: Yes, thank you. Everybody's fine.
    What about your family?

Answer the question. End the conversation.

  c YOU: _____ .

    YOUR FRIEND: Nice to see you too. Let's get
    together some time.

Agree. Promise to phone.

  d YOU: _____ .

    YOUR FRIEND: Yes, give me a call.

Say goodbye.

  e YOU: _____ .

    YOUR FRIEND: Bye. See you soon.

Listen to Track 96. Say your lines after the beep.

Vocabulary: transport

3 Look at the grid carefully. Find and circle:

  a nine types of transport
  b three verbs related to travel
  c two things which are useful for travelling

Use three different colours.

C	O	N	V	E	R	T	I	B	L	E
A	B	I	C	D	E	I	F	G	H	M
R	I	A	J	K	L	C	M	N	R	O
A	O	R	P	B	I	K	E	Q	I	B
V	R	T	S	U	T	E	U	V	D	I
A	W	X	Y	S	Z	T	U	B	E	L
N	A	E	I	O	U	P	L	A	N	E
J	D	R	I	V	E	A	V	I	M	H
I	K	E	C	A	F	L	E	X	I	O
S	P	A	A	L	L	E	Y	P	A	M
F	O	U	R	B	Y	F	O	U	R	E

4 Read the text. Complete the questions and write answers.

My favourite film: The Motorcycle Diaries (2004)

Walter Salles
Starring Gael García Bernal, Rodrigo de la Serna, Mía Maestre

In the 1950s, Ernesto 'Che' Guevara and his best friend, Alberto Granado were college students in Buenos Aires, Argentina. Ernesto studied Medicine and Alberto Biochemistry. After graduation they wanted to have fun and adventure: they decided to travel across South America. They travelled on an old motorcycle, a Norton 500. They rode through the Andes, along the coast of Chile, across the Atacama Desert and into the Peruvian Amazon.

They had fun, visited many places and met lots of people. But they discovered more than just beautiful places. Their experiences changed the men forever and decided their future. Alberto continued his work as a scientist; Ernesto became one of the most important revolutionaries of the 20th century.

Guevara wrote about his experiences on the trip in exercise books. These journals were made into a film, *The Motorcycle Diaries*.

a (study) What ....*did*.... Ernesto .....*study*..... ?

....

b (decide) What .... Ernesto and Alberto .... to do after they graduated?

....

c (travel) How .... they .... ?

....

d (go) Where .... they .... ?

....

e (do) What .... their experiences .... ?

....

f (become) What .... the two men .... ?

....

g (write) Where .... Ernesto .... about his experiences?

....

5 Put these words in the right order to make questions. Write answers.

a The Motorcycle Diaries / the film / see / you / Did / ? /

Q1: _Did you see the film The Motorcycle Diaries?_

A: _Yes I did. / No I didn't._

b your last holiday / Where / you / did / go / on / ? /

Q: .... ?

A: ....

c travel / How / did / you / ? /

Q: .... ?

A: ....

d go / you / Did / alone / ? /

Q: .... ?

A: ....

e do / did / you / What / there / ? /

Q: .... ?

A: ....

f take / How long / the trip / did / ? /

Q: .... ?

A: ....

g the trip / change / your life / in any way / Did / ? /

Q: .... ?

A: ....

Pronunciation: /eɪ/ and /e/

6 Write the sound /eɪ/, (say) or /e/ (said) next to the words in bold.

a Pass the **pepper** [/e/] **paper** [   ], please.
b Can you write that **letter** [   ] **later** [   ]?
c We didn't **sell** [   ] **sail** [   ] the boat.
d I can't believe he **fell** [   ] **failed** [   ].
e I have a **pen** [   ] **pain** [   ] in my hand.

7 Listen to Track 97. Underline the word in Activity 6 you hear.

Practise saying the sentences with the different words.

How did you do?

8 Find the mistakes in these sentences and correct them below.

a Where did you went last night?

.... ?

b How he went to the beach?

.... ?

c He went by foot.

....

d Did you travel alone? No, I not.

....

e How long does the trip took?

.... ?

f Do you like travelling by driving?

.... ?

Phonetics

9 Look at the phonemic symbols in the booklet. Write these words from Unit 20 in normal spelling.

a /ˈʌndəɡraʊnd/..

b /lʌndən/..

c /fʊt/..

d /ˈkærəvæn/..

e /kənˈvɜːtɪbl/..

Listen to Track 98 to check your answers.

Grammar and functions

1 Read the email. Fill in the blanks with the simple past form of the verbs in brackets.

```
○ ○ ○                        In                        ⊂⊃
⊘      ⬅      ⬅      ➡      ✎      📖      🏠      🗑      »
Delete  Reply  Reply All  Forward  Compose  Mailboxes  Get Mail  Junk
```

Subject: Last weekend

Hi Amanda,

We **a** .... (have) an awful experience on Sunday.
We **b** .... (go) to a safari park. We **c** ....
(drive) around and **d** .... (see) lots of animals:
lions, giraffes and even a rhino! They **e** .... (be)
great!
Then we **f** .... (go) to see the monkeys. We
drove into their special area and the car **g** ....
(stop). Ruth **h** .... (want) to feed the animals.
She **i** .... (open) the window and **j** ....
(give) them some nuts. It **k** .... (not be) a good
idea: lots of monkeys **l** .... (come) and
m .... (climb) all over the car! Ruth **n** ....
(shut) the window quickly. The monkeys **o** ....
(jump) on the roof. They **p** .... (make) a horrible
noise and they **q** .... (break) the mirrors. We
r .... (not know) what to do. John **s** ....
(phone) the guards on his mobile. They **t** ....
(come) and **u** .... (help) us. It was a terrible day!

2 Fill in the blanks.

a Q: *Did Katya go* to Africa to see wild animals?

A: No, she .... to Africa.

She .... to a safari park.

b Q: What animals .... there?

A: She ....

c Q: .... she .... a good time?

A: ....

d Q: .... the monkeys .... into the car?

A: No, they .... They .... onto the roof.

3 Write signs of warning for the safari park. Use the warnings and the imperative forms of the verbs.

Example: *Be careful! Don't stop your car.*

Be careful!	Stay feed open
Mind the .... !	switch off drive
Look out!	

Which rules did Katya and her friends break?

4 Have a conversation with Katya about her weekend. Use sequence markers.

KATYA: Hi! How are you?

YOU: *Fine thanks* . How was your weekend?

KATYA: Well, on Sunday we went to a safari park.

YOU: (approve) ....

KATYA: Yes, we like safari parks too. *First* .... we saw lions, and a rhino. We took lots of photos.

YOU: (approve) ....

KATYA: .... we went to see the monkeys.

YOU: (disapprove) ....

KATYA: Oh, I like monkeys but they climbed all over the car, and broke the mirrors.

YOU: (disapprove) .... What happened after that?

KATYA: Well, John called for help. .... , the guards came and helped us.

YOU: (end conversation. Say you'll call.)

....

KATYA: Yes, call me. And you can see my photos!

YOU: (say goodbye) ....

🎧 **Listen to Track 99. Speak after the beep.**

Review: Vocabulary

WORD LIST

admission animals astronaut autumn awful
become behead bird bring in Blackberry boat
breathe brochure caravan cat chewing gum
circle civil war cloud cloudy club convertible
costume date degrees Celsius die dog East
elephant feed female flash photography
four-by-four (4x4) get paid giraffe gladiator
historical events horse ice Iceland icy
independence kangaroo king lion lock
Look out! mail make up mobile home moon
mouse New Zealand opening hours penguin
pet petrol President Prime Minister queen
rabbit rain rat rectangle revolution
rhinoceros Roman rude snow soldier spring
square squirrel straight line summer sun
sunshine tiger transport triangle tube turn on
underground vehicle war warm weather
wedding west wild animal win wind windy
winter zoo

5 Spider diagrams can be useful because you can add more words. Make a spider diagram in your vocabulary notebook for the animals in the wordlist.

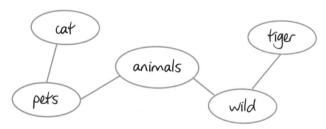

6 Writing sentences with new words helps you remember them better. Look up words related to historical events in the wordlist. Write the words and a sentence in your vocabulary notebook.

Example: President– The president of my country is (+name)

Review: Pronunciation

7 Put these regular verbs in the past simple form and write them in the table. Clue: think about their final sound, not their spelling!

breathe ◆ decide ◆ invite ◆ laugh ◆ play ◆ turn
watch ◆ behead ◆ die ◆ jump ◆ look ◆ practise
want ◆ cook ◆ end ◆ kiss ◆ love ◆ travel ◆ wash

Verbs ending in the sounds /f/, /k/, /p/, /s/, /ʃ/ and /tʃ/:   *-ed* = /t/   cooked
Verbs ending in the sounds /d/ or /t/:   *-ed* = /ɪd/   beheaded
All other verbs: *-ed* = /d/   breathed

◁)) Listen to Track 100 to check your answers.

8 Complete the table with words from these sentences.

a The plural of mouse is mice. What's the plural of house?
b Waiter! Can I have some pepper and ketchup for my steak?
c Hey, let's have white bread, not brown.
d Can I get paid now?
e How many tigers had babies in July?

/aɪ/	/aʊ/	/e/	/eɪ/
mice	mouse	pepper	waiter

◁)) Listen to Track 101 to check your answers.

9 Listen to Track 102. Underline the stressed word
◁)) in the sentences in Activity 8. Practise reading the sentences with the correct sounds and stress.

Grammar: *going to* future
(affirmative, negative and *yes/no* questions)

1 Fill in the blanks with the correct form of *going to* future of the verbs in brackets.

Do you love Cowden? Do you like green spaces?

Cowden Field is a beautiful green space. But it **a** *isn't going to be* (not be) green or beautiful anymore. They **b** .... (cut) down the trees. They **c** .... (build) a shopping mall and a big car park.

We don't want a shopping mall. Our children **d** .... (not have) a safe place to play in. Cowden **e** .... (not have) enough green spaces. There **f** .... (be) more traffic and Cowden **g** .... (not be) a quiet village anymore.

The building company says it's good for Cowden because we **h** .... (have) many good shops and many people **i** .... (get) jobs in the shops. We don't agree.

Come to the Town Hall on 25th July to give your opinion.

2 Write questions and answers about the advert.

a Cowden Field / always be green?

  Is Cowden Field always going to be green ? *No, it isn't* .

b the building company / keep the trees?

  .... ? ....

c many people / work in the shopping mall?

  .... ? ....

d people in Cowden / enjoy the shopping mall?

  .... ? ....

e the children / play safely?

  .... ? ....

f shoppers / have a place to park their cars?

  .... ? ....

3 At the Town Hall. Ask the building company five questions. Use *going to*.

a plant new trees? *Are you going to plant new trees?*

b car park free? ....

c special area for children? ....

e shopping mall open on Sundays? ....

f build shopping mall this year? ....

Vocabulary: geography

4 Listen to Track 103. Match the conversations with the pictures.

Conversation ....

Conversation ....

Now label the pictures with words in the box.

beach ◆ cave ◆ cliffs ◆ forest
island ◆ mountain ◆ river ◆ sea
village

Pronunciation: /iː/ and /ɪ/

5 Write the words underlined in the chart according to their sound /iː/, (*sheep*), or /ɪ/, like (*ship*).

a <u>Sit</u> down and <u>eat</u> your <u>meat</u>.
b <u>Please</u> take a <u>seat</u>, <u>Phil</u>.
c <u>Tim</u>'s <u>team</u> is going to <u>win</u>.
d <u>Listen</u> and <u>fill</u> in the blanks on your <u>sheet</u>.
e <u>This</u> <u>machine</u>'s very quick.

/ɪ/	/iː/
sit	eat

Listen to Track 104 to check your answers. Practise reading the sentences aloud.

Function: expressing hope

6 Match the questions with the answers. Then write true answers for yourself.

a Is this going to be a good year for you?
b Is it going to rain this afternoon?
c What are you going to do next weekend?
d Where are you travelling this year?

1 I hope (that) I can go to New York.
2 I hope (that) I have time to go shopping.
3 I hope so! Keep your fingers crossed!
4 I hope not. I want to play tennis.

a	b	c	d
3			

7 Write responses.

a I have a stomach ache.

   I hope you feel better soon.

b I have an English test tomorrow.

   ....

c Thank you very much for my present.

   ....

d We're going to visit your country!

   ....

e We're going to be there in July. Is it going to rain, do you think?

   ....

f Do you think we're going to like the food?

   ....

Listen to track 105. Respond after the beep.

How did you do?

8 Translate these sentences into your language.

a Be careful! The glass is going to fall.

   ....

b They aren't going to visit the island.

   ....

c I hope you can come to my party.

   ....

d Are you going to walk to the gym?

   ....

e I hope not!

   ....

f I hope so! Keep your fingers crossed!

   ....

Phonetics

9 Look at the phonemic symbols in the booklet. Write these words from Unit 21 in normal spelling.

a /həʊp/ ....

b /ˈvɪlɪdʒ/ ....

c /ˈtreʒə/ ....

d /təˈmɒrəʊ/ ....

e /ˈfɪŋgəz/ ....

Listen to Track 106 to check your answers.

UNIT 22 Entertainment

Vocabulary: places to go

1 Match the columns to make sentences.

I want to go to	the cinema a gallery the theatre the stadium a restaurant the museum the concert hall	to have to listen to to see to watch	a film. a match. a famous pianist. a meal. an exhibition. some photographs. a play.

Example: I want to go to the cinema to see / watch a film.

....

....

....

....

....

....

....

....

2 Put the words in groups.

Art • classical music • club • concert hall • dance • gallery
go clubbing • have a meal • menu • museum • opera
paintings • pop music • portraits • ~~restaurant~~ • sculpture

Entertainment			
Eating out	**Concerts**	**Exhibitions**	**Clubbing**
restaurant			

Function: making plans

3 Number the sentences 1-8 to make a conversation.

What shall we do on Saturday?	[1]
That's a good idea.	[ ]
There's a Japanese film on at the local cinema.	[ ]
Shall I go and buy the tickets?	[ ]
That sounds interesting. Let's do that.	[ ]
Is there anything good on?	[ ]
Why don't we go to the cinema?	[ ]
You don't go have to go and buy the tickets. You can buy them on the phone.	[ ]

Listen to Track 107 to check your answers.

4 Talk to Irina on the Internet about your weekend plans.

IRINA: Wow! It's the weekend, finally! What are you going to do tomorrow?

YOU: I'm going to ....

IRINA: That sounds good. What are your plans for Sunday?

YOU: ....
What about you?

IRINA: I'm going to go to a pop concert.

YOU: ....

IRINA: Shall we talk again next week?

YOU: ....

IRINA: Well, have a good weekend!

YOU: ....

Listen to Track 108. Talk after the beep.

5 Read the leaflet. Answer the questions.

   a Which places are open now?
   b Which places are going to open in the future?

Welcome to
The Melting Pot Arts Centre
Things are great at the Melting Pot and they're going to get better.

Now open: Screens 1 and 2 for the best international cinema, old and new.

Coming in the autumn: Bollywood Festival, exciting films from India for all the family.

Food village: Food from around the world.

Here are some examples: *Mamma Mia*, food from the South of Italy. Don't miss the ice cream week in October!
Chinatown, the best Cantonese food in town. Special All-you-can-eat deal from 23-30 October (lunch time only).

Coming soon: Concert Hall: Hot reggae band The Urban Rats (September 15-17) Dixiejazz, jazz from New Orleans (October 1-4).

The Circle Art Gallery: The gallery is going to open in October with an exhibition of African Modern Art, the best artists from the African continent. In November, 'People of the world in Britain', a photography exhibition.

6 Write questions and answers about future events at the arts centre using *is/are going to*.

   a When / the Bollywood Festival / start?
   When is the Bollywood Festival going to start? ?
   ....

   b Who / play / at the Concert Hall / in October?
   .... ?
   ....

   c When / the reggae band / play?
   .... ?
   ....

   d What / special event / there / be / at *Mamma Mia*?
   .... ?
   ....

   e How long / the special deal at Chinatown / last?
   .... ?
   ....

   f How many / new places / open / at the Melting Pot?
   .... ?
   ....

   g What month / The Circle Art Gallery / open?
   .... ?
   ....

   h Where / the exhibition of African Art / be?
   .... ?
   ....

a Open now:
   Screens 1 and 2
   ....
   ....

b Open in the future:
   ....
   ....
   ....

Pronunciation: /tuː/ and /tə/ in *going to*

7 Choose the correct pronunciation.

   a Aren't you going to /tuː/ /tə/ answer the phone?

   b There's going to /tuː/ /tə/ be a jazz concert in September.

   c I'm going to /tuː/ /tə/ ask Jamie to come.

   d Who are you going to /tuː/ /tə/ invite?

   e Where are The Urban Rats going to /tuː/ /tə/ play?

   f When is the new gallery going to /tuː/ /tə/ open?

Listen to Track 109 to check your answers.

How did you do?

8 Find the mistakes in these sentences and correct them below.

   a What you are going to do in the summer?

   .... ?

   b Does he going to buy tickets for the concert?

   .... ?

   c What shall we to do on Sunday?

   .... ?

   d Why don't we watching television?

   .... ?

   e Yes, let's to do that.

   ....

   f When are you go to see that film?

   .... ?

Phonetics

9 Look at the phonemic symbols in the booklet. Write these words from Unit 22 in normal spelling.

   a /ˈgælərɪ/ ....

   b /kæfəˈtɪrɪə/ ....

   c /ˈrestrɒnt/ ....

   d /θɪətə/ ....

   e /entəˈteɪnmənt/ ....

Listen to Track 110 to check your answers.

UNIT 23 Comparing and buying

Vocabulary: adjectives

1 Match the nouns on the right with the adjectives on the left. You must use each adjective only once.

Adjectives	Nouns
beautiful handsome high long narrow tall thick thin	man wall street person tree building woman snake

A beautiful woman

....

....

....

....

....

2 Complete the sentences with the opposite of the adjectives in brackets.

a This car is very ......*cheap*...... . (expensive)

b My cousin wears very

.... clothes. (modern)

c Juan is quite .... (handsome)

d The roads in this city are very

.... (narrow)

e Frankly, I think Joanne is quite

.... (beautiful)

f The walls around the garden

are quite .... (high)

g I have to go on a diet. I'm

getting a bit .... (thin)

Grammar: comparative forms of adjectives

3 Match the beginnings and ends of the rules

Comparatives: rules

a To compare similar things ...
b The comparative of adjectives of 1 or 2 syllables is ...
c The comparative form of adjectives of 2 or more syllables is ...
d When an adjective ends in 'y' ...
e When an adjective ends in one ... vowel + one consonant ...

1 *more* + adj. + *than*.
2 we double the last letter.
3 we use *as ... as*.
4 adj + *-er* + *than*.
5 we change the *y* for an *i* and add *-er*.

4 Complete the advert with the correct comparative forms.

Going on a skiing holiday?

Imagine the perfect holiday: the flight is **a** (+short) *shorter than* your journey to work. The hotel is **b** (=comfortable) .... your own home. The mountains are **c** (+beautiful) .... the pictures in the brochure. Skiing is **d** (+easy) .... walking. You're a natural. You're **e** (=fast) .... the wind down the mountain. But accidents happen: you fall and break your leg. A night in hospital can be **f** (+expensive) .... a night in a luxury hotel. Travel insurance isn't **g** (=expensive) .... you think. Getaround travel insurance. It's **h** (+cheap) .... a meal out.

5 Write comparative sentences. Use adjectives in Activities 1 and 2.

a The Amazon, Brazil
The Thames, England
The Amazon is wider than the Thames. The Thames isn't as wide as the Amazon.

b The Great Pyramid of Cheops, Egypt
The Eiffel Tower, Paris ....

c The European continent
The American continent ....

d Brad Pitt
George Clooney ....

e Angelina Jolie
Scarlet Johansson ....

Function: comparing things

6 Listen to Ella and Jesper on Track 111 discussing their plans for a party. What does Ella think of these things? Use the phrases in the boxes.

too	big spicy hot small soon boring	(not)	big exciting large	enough	cooler better

a the beach *It's too hot.*

b the house ....

c the garden ....

d Indian food ....

e Italian food ....

f a barbecue ....

g sending invitations ....

Where are they going to have the party? What are they going to eat?

They are going to have the party in the garden.

....

....

....

....

7 You are going out with a friend. Choose the idea you like best. Give reasons for not accepting his ideas. Use *too*, *enough*, *not enough* or a comparative adjective.

YOUR FRIEND: What kind of movie do you want to see, a romantic comedy, a western or an action film?

Example: *Let's see a romantic comedy. Westerns are too boring and action films are more boring.*

YOU: ....

....

YOUR FRIEND: What time shall we go, at 2 p.m, 6 p.m. or 10 p.m.?

YOU: ....

....

YOUR FRIEND: Shall we go to a restaurant after?

YOU: ....

....

YOUR FRIEND: OK. Do you want to walk or take a taxi? Or shall we take our bikes?

YOU: ....

....

YOUR FRIEND: OK. See you later.

Listen to Track 112. Say your lines after the beep.

Pronunciation: stress in comparative sentences

8 Read the sentences. Underline the words that are stressed in sentences a – f.

Listen to Track 113 to check your answers.

a Beaches are hotter than mountains.
b This book's more interesting than that one.
c Bob's shorter than Peter.
d He's more attractive than Peter.
e Miranda's as clever as Tim.
f Today is better than yesterday and not as good as tomorrow.

Now complete the rule.

In comparative sentences we usually stress the important words: the *comparative adjective* and the things we are comparing. Contractions and the words .... , ... , ... , ... and .... are not usually stressed.

How did you do?

9 Translate these sentences into your language.

a The capital of my country is bigger than London.

....

b Museums are more interesting than clubs.

....

c Is your language as easy as English?

....

d This room isn't big enough for a party.

....

e Open the windows. It's too hot in here.

....

f There aren't any high mountains here but there are some tall buildings.

....

Phonetics

10 Look at the phonemic symbols in the booklet. Write these words form Unit 23 in normal spelling.

a /ˈbaɪjɪŋ/ ....
b /ˈprɪtɪə/ ....
c /ˈʌnətræktɪv/ ....
d /ˈbjuːtɪfəl/ ....

Listen to Track 114 to check your answers.

UNIT 24 Technology

Function: asking and giving opinions

1 Match the opinions and the responses.

Opinions
a Older people can't use technology.
b I think technology is important in medicine.
c The world is better thanks to technology, don't you agree?
d Old people hate computers.
e Blackberries are better than mobile phones.

Responses
1 That's right. It is a better place.
2 I agree but it is important for other things too.
3 You're right, but they're more expensive.
4 You're wrong. Anyone can learn.
5 I don't agree. My grandmother emails her friends.

a	b	c	d	e
3				

2 Respond to these people's opinions. Give reasons.

a I think robots that clean the house are a really good idea. What do you think?

YOU: *That's wrong. Robots are a silly idea.*

b Computers are better than people. They don't make mistakes, don't you agree?

YOU: ....

c Big, fast cars in big cities are a really bad idea, don't you think?

YOU: ....

d I think cycling is better than driving. Do you agree with me?

YOU: ....

e Space travel doesn't do anything good for people.

YOU: ....

f Listen to this in the paper: 'Computer games are bad for children'. Do you agree with that?

YOU: ....

Now listen to Track 115. Say your lines after the beep.

Vocabulary: technology

3 What is it? Write the name of the gadgets in the spaces.

a It's a camera. It doesn't need any film.

A d.*igital* .... c.*amera* ....

b It's a screen. It is flat. You can hang it on the wall.

A p.................... s...................

c It's small. You can put it on your knees. It's a computer.

A l.................... c....................

d It's a telephone. You normally use it at home. It has no wires.

A c.................... p....................

e It can go in your pocket. It has many buttons. It has email and Internet connection.

A B....................

f It records programmes. It uses DVDs. It can have a hard disc.

A D.................... r....................

g It's only about 6 cm. It's plastic. It stores computer documents.

A m.................... s....................

h It's a television. It's quite new. It has a fantastic picture.

A H.................... D....................

t....................

4 Which of the things in Activity 3 are good for these actions? Write the name.

a Take photos:

a digital camera

b Watch TV:

....

c Email:

....

d Work on planes:

....

e Save your work:

....

f Phone from the garden:

....

Grammar: present, past and future tenses

5 Put the time expressions in groups. Be careful! Some expressions can go in more than one group

> ago ◆ at the moment ◆ at night ◆ at 8 o'clock ◆ every day in 2001 ◆ last week ◆ never ◆ next week ◆ now ◆ on Sundays soon ◆ this week ◆ tomorrow ◆ usually ◆ yesterday

Present continuous	Present simple	Past simple	*Going to* future
at the moment	at night	ago	next week

6 Read the interview. Fill in the blanks with the correct form of the verbs in brackets: present simple, present continuous, past simple or *going to* future.

The interview

Emmy Hurtado, young businesswoman of the year

What does your company do?
We **a** .... (buy) beautiful objects from other countries, like rugs from Mexico and baskets from the Philippines. We **b** .... (sell) them in London.

What's special about your company?
We **c** .... (help) communities in poor countries.
We **d** .... (pay) them a good price for their objects and we sell them at good prices here. Everybody **e** ....(wins)!

How did your business start?
I **f** .... (go) to my family's village in the Philippines on holiday. I **g** .... (see) some beautiful baskets. I **h** .... (talk) to the people. They wanted to do business in other countries but they **i** .... (not have) enough money and they **j** .... (not have) any contacts. We **k** .... (give) them the money to start and we **l** .... (sell) their baskets here.

What are your plans for the future?
Next year we **m** .... (open) a new shop in Scotland.
We **n** .... (look) for a place now.

7 Use these prompts to ask Emmy questions about her business. Think about the tenses you need and the question forms.

a When / you / go / to the Philippines / ? /

When did you go to the Philippines ?

b you / start / your business alone / ? /

.... ?

c Who / work with / you / ? /

.... ?

d you / sell / things from India / ? /

.... ?

e you / plan / to open more shops / ? /

.... ?

f How / your business / do / at the moment / ? /

.... ?

g What country / you / visit / next / ? /

.... ?

h you / sell / clothes / ? /

.... ?

Pronunciation: /e/, /æ/, /ʌ/ and /ɜː/

8 Say these words aloud. Write them in the table, according to their pronunciation.

bad ◆ bed ◆ bird ◆ cat ◆ cut ◆ does ◆ love ◆ man
marry ◆ men ◆ money ◆ tan ◆ ten ◆ turn
wedding ◆ won ◆ word ◆ work ◆ world

/e/	/æ/	/ʌ/	/ɜː/
bed	bad	cut	bird

Listen to Track 116 to check your answers.

How did you do?

9 Find the mistakes in these sentences and correct them below.

a I am not agree with you.

....

b I am watching television last night.

....

c Does your class uses a computer?

.... ?

d Did you bought a new plasma screen?

.... ?

e I am going seeing the technology show tomorrow.

....

f I got my first laptop in two months ago.

....

Phonetics

10 Look at the phonemic symbols in the booklet. Write these words form Unit 24 in normal spelling.

a /əˈgəʊ/ ....

b /ˈdɪdʒɪtl/ ....

c /tekˈnɒlədʒɪ/ ....

d /ˈpaːmtɒp/ ....

e /ˈɪntəvjuː/ ....

Listen to Track 117 to check your answers.

Grammar and functions

1 Samira is from Malaysia. She's asking Rosie, an English friend, about English weddings. Fill in the blanks with the simple present form of the verbs in brackets.

SAMIRA: What do you call the man and the woman in a wedding?

ROSIE: She's the bride and he's the bridegroom.

AMIRA: **a** ....*Does*.... the bride **b** ...*wear*.... (wear) special clothes?

ROSIE: Yes, she **c** .... She usually **d** .... (wear) a white dress.

SAMIRA: Who are the other important people?

ROSIE: The bridegroom **e** .... (invite) a friend to be his 'best man'. He **f** .... (carry) the rings and **g** .... (stand) next to the bridegroom in the ceremony.

SAMIRA: **h** .... the bride **i** .... (have) a friend too?

ROSIE: Yes, she's the maid of honour.

AMIRA: What **j** .... people **k** .... (do) after the ceremony?

ROSIE: They **l** .... (have) a reception, a party. After the party the bride and groom **m** .... (go) on holiday. It's their honeymoon.

Are weddings the same in your country? Write three sentences about weddings in your country.

The bride wears red.

....

....

....

....

2 Look at the wedding invitation. Answer Samira's questions about a wedding you are going to.

SAMIRA: What are your plans for next Saturday?

YOU: **a** *I'm going to go to a wedding.*

SAMIRA: That's nice. Where is it going to be?

YOU: **b** ....

SAMIRA: Are they going to have a reception?

YOU: **c** ....

SAMIRA: Is it going to be at their house?

YOU: **d** ....

SAMIRA: Are you going to buy them a present?

YOU: **e** ....

SAMIRA: Do you have time for a coffee before the party?

YOU: **f** ....

SAMIRA: Well, have a good time!

Nicole Johnston
and
Paul Woods

begin a new life together
on Saturday 19th August at 11.00 a.m.
at Chelsea Town Hall

followed by a reception at
The Riverside Hotel from 6.00 p.m.

Please join us on this special day.

RSVP: 93756006

◁)) Listen to Track 118. Speak after the beep.

3 Complete the conversations with phrases and sentences from the box.

~~What shall I wear to the wedding?~~ ◆ I hope so.
I hope not! ◆ That's not nice enough for a wedding.
Hmm, I suppose so. ◆ No, I don't agree. That's silly.
You're right. Let's agree to disagree.
Well, it's very expensive.

SAMIRA: **a** *What shall I wear to the wedding?*

JAMES: Why don't you wear your white dress?

SAMIRA: Only the bride wears white. She's more important than all the other women that day, so I think that's right, don't you agree?

JAMES: **b** _____

SAMIRA: You're wrong!

JAMES: Oh, it isn't important.

SAMIRA: **c** _____

SAMIRA: What are you going to wear to the wedding?

JAMES: Jeans, a T-shirt and a jacket.

SAMIRA: **d** _____

JAMES: OK. Jeans, a shirt and a jacket?

SAMIRA: **e** _____

SAMIRA: Is the wedding going to be fun?

NICOLE: **f** _____

SAMIRA: Are you going to have children soon?

NICOLE: **g** _____

SAMIRA: Are you planning to live in this area?

NICOLE: **h** _____ but I hope we can find a cheap flat. Keep your fingers crossed!

🔊 Listen to Track 119 to check your answers.

4 Complete the best man's speech with the correct form of the verbs in brackets, present continuous, present simple, past simple or *going to* future.

Dear friends, we **a** *are celebrating* (celebrate) today Paul and Nicole's new life together.

I **b** _____ (meet) Paul on our first day at high school. We **c** _____ (do) everything together. We **d** _____ (study) together, we **e** _____ (have) fun together and we **f** _____ (not fall) in love together, but at the same time. One day he **g** _____ (say):

h '_____ (do) you _____ (remember) Nicole from high school?'

He **i** _____ (not have to) say more.

I **j** _____ (know) this **k** _____ (be) real love.

So, in the future **l** I' _____ (do) everything with Paul AND Nicole! And the first thing we **m** _____ (do) is drink to their happiness. Nicole and Paul!

🔊 Listen to Track 120 to check your answers.

WORD LIST

annual award-winning barbecue beach beautiful
brand new bungee jump cache cave cinema
classical music cliff club collection concert hall
contestant cordless phone crash cutlery detect
detergent digital camera dinner service discovery
DVD player DVD recorder earn money eat out
embarrassing entertainment exhibition fall
forest gallery get married go clubbing handsome
hard disk health check-up high
High Definition television hopes (n) hope (v)
insurance invitation island knob lifestyle
logbook long low match memory stick
mental health modern mountain movie museum
narrow old-fashioned palmtop computer
peace of mind picnic plain plans plasma screen
play (n) playwright pool table press (v) restaurant
river robot sea stadium stage stay in
tailor-made tall technology theatre thick thin
toaster treasure treasure hunt unattractive
village vital western (n) wide

5 Write new words with their 'partners'; words that often go together.

Use a dictionalry to look up words related to 'Entertainment' (e.g. theatre). Write the words with their partners.

Example: to go the theatre to see a play.
Playwrights write plays.

6 Writing examples can help you remember new words better. Find words related to 'Geography' in the word list. Write the words with an example.

Example: beach – e.g. Miami Beach
Island – e.g. Hawaii

....
....
....
....
....

Review: Pronunciation

7 Write these words form the wordlist in the table according to their sound.

beach ◆ bungee ◆ check-up ◆ cliff ◆ club ◆ concert
contestant ◆ crash ◆ cutlery ◆ detergent ◆ digital
disk ◆ earn ◆ eat ◆ health ◆ jump ◆ match
memory ◆ modern ◆ narrow ◆ peace ◆ picnic
plans ◆ plasma ◆ press ◆ river ◆ sea ◆ service
treasure

/iː/	beach
/ɪ/	cliff
/e/	check-up
/æ/	crash
/ʌ/	bungee
/ɜː/	concert

Can you add more words from the wordlist?

Listen to Track 121 to check your answers.

8 Listen to Track 122.

Underline the words that are stressed in the comparative sentences.

Write /tuː/ or /tə/ in the spaces.

a My car's older than yours. I'm going to [/tə/] buy a new one.
b This room's hotter than the Sahara! I'm going to [ ] open the windows.
c This film's more interesting than the others. I'm going to [ ] ask Molly to come.
d This camera's not as good as that one. I'm going to [ ] get a digital one.

Listen to Track 122 to check your answers. Practise saying the sentences with the correct pronunciation and stress.

Audioscript

Track 1
WOMAN: Hello. I'm Helena. What's your name?
BEEP:
WOMAN: Nice to meet you.
BEEP:
WOMAN: This is my friend Marco.
BEEP:
MAN: Hi. How are you?
BEEP:

Track 2
A H J I
B C D E F G P V X
K Q U W
Y I T
L M N R S

Track 3
1 H-i (twice)
2 t-h-i-s
3 m-e-e-t
4 n-i-c-e
5 a-r-e
6 h-o-w
7 y-o-u
8 i-s
9 A-n-n-i-e
10 B-e-n
11 t-o

Track 4
YOUNG MAN: Ben, this is Annie.
YOUNG MAN 2: Hi. How are you?
YOUNG WOMAN: Nice to meet you Ben.

Track 5
a who
b what
c this
d I'm
e They're

Track 6
MAN: Who are you?
BEEP
MAN: Where are you from?
BEEP
MAN: What's your nationality?
BEEP
MAN: What colour's the flag of your country?
BEEP
MAN: What are the names of the countries near your country?
BEEP
MAN: What colour are their flags?
BEEP
MAN: What's your favourite colour?
BEEP
MAN: Really? That's my favourite colour too!

Track 7
a Australia
b Brazil
c Canada
d China
e Japan
f Korea
g Mexico
h Russia

Track 8
a Korean
b Australian
c colour
d aren't
e isn't

Track 9
BEEP
WOMAN: Sure. What's your first name?
BEEP
WOMAN: Right. What's your last name?
BEEP
WOMAN: What's your telephone number?
BEEP
WOMAN: Do you have email?
BEEP
WOMAN: OK. I'll send you the information right away.
BEEP

Track 10
a Danny's a dancer.
b Pat's an accountant.
c Len's a taxi driver.
d Is Kim a singer?
e She isn't a painter.

Track 11
a job
b accountant
c street
d student
e teacher

Track 12
a Frida and Nadia are mother and daughter.
b Fred's a good brother.
c Their father's over there.
d Read this today and that on Monday.

Track 13
a son
b years
c cousin
d these
e this

Track 14

MAN: Hello agent 999.

MAN 2: Sorry? I'm not an agent. My name's Ben Murphy. I'm a taxi driver. Who are you?

MAN: I'm Blond, Jim Blond. Hey, where is Mona O'Hara?

MAN 2: Mona O'Hara? Who is she?

MAN: Come on Murphy, you know. She's our woman in Cambridge, of course.

Track 15

MAN: Ah, here is Mona. Good evening, Mona.

MAN 2: She isn't Mona. She's my friend Lara. Lara, this is Jim Blond. He's an agent.

WOMAN: That's interesting. Nice to meet you Jim.

MAN: Nice to meet you too, Mona. You're very young! How old are you?

WOMAN: I'm 17 years old.

MAN: Agents are very young these days.

Track 16

MAN: Where are you from, Lara?

WOMAN: I'm from Australia. You're American, right?

MAN: Of course not! I'm British. Where is Murphy from? Is he Australian too?

WOMAN: Ben? No, he isn't. He's from Canada.

MAN: Ah, Canadian. Canadians are good agents.

Track 17

MAN: Look at those people over there.

WOMAN: Oh, are they your friends?

MAN: Shhh! No, they aren't. They're Lorry and Harry. They're really bad. And that's their car.

WOMAN: Well, this is our car. And these are the keys. Come on, let's go.

MAN 2: No, Lara! Look Jim, we aren't really agents.

WOMAN: We are now!

Track 18

BEEP

WOMAN: Lara

BEEP

WOMAN: Jones. That's J-O-N-E-S. Jones.

BEEP

WOMAN: I'm Australian.

BEEP

WOMAN: I'm 17 years old.

BEEP

WOMAN: 22 Elm Street. E-L-M, Elm Street.

BEEP

WOMAN: My phone number is 0208 576 6892,

BEEP

WOMAN: My email is lara@myhouse.com

Track 19

a A, H, J, K,

b B, C, D, E, G, P, T, V

c F, L, M, N, S, X,

d Q, U

Track 20

Canada

Canadian

Japan

Japanese

China

Chinese

Track 21

A words with the sound /ə/: brother, a, doctor, father, mother, Canada, Japan

B words with the sound /d/: doctor, dad, Canada, Canadian, friend, dentist, daughter, red

C words with the sound /ð/: brother, father, mother, these, those, they

Track 22

WOMAN: Hi! I'm Stella, from Manchester, in the UK. Where are you from?

BEEP

WOMAN: In Britain we work from 9.00 to 5.00. What about you?

BEEP

WOMAN: I go to work by bus. People here read the paper or a book on the bus. What about you?

BEEP

WOMAN: Here shops open from 10.00 to 6.00. I go shopping on Saturdays or Sundays. And you?

BEEP

WOMAN: I go to my Spanish class on Wednesdays from 6.00 to 8.00. When is your English class?

BEEP

WOMAN: Well, nice to meet you. Bye.

BEEP

Track 23

a Peter watches television and Sue reads the paper.

b Ken works all day and relaxes in the evening.

c Sue puts the baby in its bed, she kisses it and then goes to bed.

d She sleeps and she gets up when the baby cries.

Track 24

a doesn't (twice)

b goes

c minutes

d don't

e Wednesday

Track 25

WOMAN: It's 1 o'clock- lunchtime! In Britain we have a small meal at lunch and a big meal in the evening. What about your country?

BEEP

WOMAN: I like to have tea, milk and bread for breakfast. And you?

BEEP

WOMAN: What about lunch? I like a sandwich and some fruit.

BEEP

WOMAN: Dinner is at 7.00. We have meat or fish and vegetables. What about you?

BEEP

WOMAN: I like snacks in the afternoon, chocolate for example. How about you?

BEEP

WOMAN: Back to work now. Talk to you soon!

Track 26

a What do you like for lunch?
b Do you eat snacks?
c Do you like fish?
d Does your family eat together?
e Do people in your country eat rice?

Track 27

WOMAN: Can I help you?
MAN: I'd like a cheese sandwich and a chocolate ice cream, please.
WOMAN: What would you like to drink?
MAN: I'll have a cup of coffee. Milk, no sugar.
WOMAN: Anything else?
MAN: No thank you.
WOMAN: That's £5.20, please.

Track 28

BEEP
WOMAN: I'll have a chicken salad and a chocolate cake, please.
BEEP
WOMAN: I'd like an orange juice.
BEEP
WOMAN: That's all, thank you.

Track 29

a orange
b juice
c fish and chips
d tomato
e bread and butter

Track 30

a What's your name?
b Do you live here?
c Where do you live?
d When do you go shopping?
e Do you like travelling?
f Does he work in a bank?

Track 31

MAN: We love playing soccer. It's fun.
WOMAN: I agree. It's great fun.

WOMAN: Ronaldinho is Mexican, right.
MAN: Certainly not. He's Brazilian.

MAN: You like going shopping, don't you.
WOMAN: Of course I do.

WOMAN: Susie really likes doing puzzles.
MAN: No, that's not right. She likes reading.

Track 32

a You like travelling, don't you?
BEEP
b English is fun.
BEEP
c Shakira is French, right?
BEEP
d I like Chinese food. It's delicious.
BEEP

Track 33

a sometimes
b usually
c always
d occasionally

Track 34

MAN: What's the matter with Janie?
WOMAN: Her throat hurts.
MAN: Poor Janie.
WOMAN: What's wrong with Billy?
MAN: He's got a problem.
WOMAN: Oh, dear. Poor Billy.
MAN: How do you feel?
WOMAN: I feel awful. My head hurts.
MAN: You poor thing!

Track 35

MAN: What's the matter with Janie?
BEEP
MAN: Poor Janie.
BEEP
MAN: He's got a problem.
BEEP
MAN: How do you feel?
BEEP
MAN: You poor thing!

Track 36

a	tree	three
b	tree	tree
c	three	three
d	both	both
e	boat	both
f	boat	boat
g	thin	tin
h	tin	tin
i	thin	thin

Track 37

a foot
b throat
c mouth
d tooth

Track 38

JUSTINE: What's the matter with Klaus?
MARTIN: He's hungry.
JUSTINE: Why doesn't he have lunch?
MARTIN: His tooth hurts when he eats.
JUSTINE: Oh dear. Poor Klaus.

DAVE: Do you like getting up early?
JULIA: No, I hate it, but I start work at quarter past seven.
DAVE: Oh. So what time do you get up?
JULIA: At half past six.
DAVE: That's awful. Getting up early is difficult.
JULIA: Yes, I agree.

Track 39

Nouns that contain the sound /t/: basketball, breakfast, carton, chest, chocolate, foot, football, fruit, meat, packet, skateboarding, stomach, tennis, throat, travelling, tuna, vegetables, watching TV, working out
Nouns that contain the sound /θ/: mouth, throat, tooth

Track 40

a Do you get up early on Saturdays?
b What time do you go to bed?
c How often do you do your homework?
d Where do you live?
e Does she live in France?
f Are they German?

Track 41

/z/ goes to bed, flies, has a shower, studies
/s/ gets up, meets, sleeps, works
/ɪz/ relaxes, washes, watches

Track 42

Conversation 1
CUSTOMER: Excuse me. How much is this bread?
ASSISTANT: It's £1.50 a loaf.
CUSTOMER: I'll take two, please. How much is that?
ASSISTANT: That's £3.00. Anything else?
CUSTOMER: No, thank you.

Conversation 2
CUSTOMER: I'd like a dress.
ASSISTANT: Certainly. What about this black one?
CUSTOMER: How much does it cost?
ASSISTANT: £50. Do you want to try it?
CUSTOMER: Yes, please.

Track 43

WOMAN: Excuse me. How much is that chicken?
BEEP
WOMAN: Two kilos, please.
BEEP
WOMAN: No, thank you.

Track 44

a How many apples do you want?
b How much bread do you want?
c How many eggs do you want?
d How much salad do you want?
e How much does this meat cost?
f How many bananas do you want?

Track 45

a shoes
b suit
c shirt
d jacket

Track 46

YOUNG WOMAN: What does 'clothes' mean?
YOUNG MAN: Things we wear.
YOUNG MAN 2: How do you say 'not very often'?
YOUNG WOMAN: Occasionally.
YOUNG WOMAN: What does 'magazine' mean?
YOUNG MAN: It's something to read and it has a lot of
    pictures.
YOUNG MAN 2: How do you say 'the part of your body
    where food goes'?
YOUNG WOMAN: Stomach.

Track 47

JOANNE: Do you want to come to the cinema with us?
KEN: Can you speak more slowly, please?
JOANNE: There's a great movie this evening.

KEN: What does 'movie' mean?
JOANNE: It's a film.
KEN: Can you say that again, please?
JOANNE: A movie is a film at the cinema.
KEN: I'd love to go to the movie!
JOANNE: Great.

Track 48

JOANNE: Do you want to come to the cinema with us?
BEEP
JOANNE: There's a great movie this evening.
BEEP
JOANNE: It's a film.
BEEP
JOANNE: A movie is a film at the cinema.
BEEP
JOANNE: Great.

Track 49

a thin
b thing
c sing
d song
e sun
f fun
g ring

Track 50

a sing
b going
c think
d thinking

Track 51

MARY: Do you know Joe?
FREDDIE: I'm not sure. What does he look like?
MARY: He's got short blond hair and blue eyes.
FREDDIE: Hmm. How tall is he?
MARY: About 1.85, I think.
FREDDIE: Is he thin? How much does he weigh?
MARY: I don't know. He's slim, maybe about 90 kilos.
FREDDIE: I think I know him. How old is he?
MARY: About 25.
FREDDIE: Oh, yes. I know him. What about him?

Track 52

BEEP
MAN: I'm not sure. What does she look like?
BEEP
MAN: Hmm. How tall is she?
BEEP
MAN: How much does she weigh?
BEEP
MAN: Yes, I think I know her. How old is she?
BEEP

Track 53

a Yes, I am watching the television.
b You're talking too much.
c She is climbing the tree.
d No, he isn't coming home for dinner.
e Yes, they are singing.
f Yes, we're coming to your party.

Track 54

a short
b long
c thin
d tall

Track 55

MARIANA: Hello?
FERNANDO: Hello.
MARIANA: Can I speak to Lyndsay, please?
FERNANDO: She's not here. Who's speaking?
MARIANA: It's Mariana.
FERNANDO: Do you want to leave a message?
MARIANA: Yes, please. Can you tell her that Mariana and
    Robin aren't coming to the party, because Robin is sick?
FERNANDO: Sure, I'll tell her.
MARIANA: Thanks. Bye.
FERNANDO: Bye.

Track 56

MARIANA: Hello?
BEEP
MARIANA: Can I speak to Lyndsay, please?
BEEP
MARIANA: It's Mariana.
BEEP
MARIANA: Yes, please. Can you tell her that Mariana and
    Robin aren't coming to the party, because Robin is sick?
BEEP
MARIANA: Thanks. Bye.
BEEP

Track 57

a boss
b bus
c hut
d hot
e cup
f cop
g song
h sung

Track 58

a love
b money
c does
d boss

Track 59

LISA: Hello? Can I speak to Marty, please?
STEVE: He's not here. Who's speaking?
LISA: It's Lisa.
STEVE: Hi Lisa! Do you want to leave a message?
LISA: Yes. Can you tell him to pick up my sister, Candy, from
    the airport?
STEVE: OK.
LISA: She's tall and she's got long dark hair and dark eyes.
    She's not very thin.
STEVE: Ok ... tall, long dark hair ... not very thin. I'll tell him.
LISA: Thanks, Steve. Bye.
STEVE: Bye.

Track 60

Adjectives and nouns that contain the sound /ʌ/: chubby, club,
fun
Nouns that contain the sound /ɒ/: blond, contact, costumes,
long, sock

Track 61

a How much is that shirt?
b Can you speak slowly, please?
c She's got dark brown hair.
d He's got light blue eyes.
e Can I take a message?
f How much does it cost?

Track 62

/n/ machine, present, blonde, carnival, contact, dance, Internet,
    fun, magazine, phone, organise, send, thin
/ŋ/ answering, having, interacting, length, sing

Track 63

a beds b chairs c desks d fridges e stoves f showers
g toilets h lamps i watches

Track 64

Conversation 1
MAN: Have you seen my watch?
WOMAN: No. Is it under the newspaper?
MAN: Where's the newspaper?
WOMAN: In the living room.
MAN: No, it isn't under the newspaper.
WOMAN: Is it in the bathroom?
MAN: Oh, yes. Here it is.

Conversation 2
WOMAN: Where are my glasses?
MAN: Are they on the fridge?
WOMAN: No, they aren't in the kitchen.
MAN: Are they in the living room?
WOMAN: Oh, yes, here they are next to the TV.

Track 65

KENNY: Have you seen my keys?
BEEP
KENNY: No, they aren't.
BEEP
KENNY: No.
BEEP
KENNY: Oh, yes. Here they are. Thanks.

Track 66

a bedrooms
b desks
c watches
d lamps
e fridges
f kitchens

Track 67

YOUNG MAN: Excuse me, is there a hospital near here?
OLD WOMAN: Yes, dear. Go straight along this street. Turn
    left onto Green St and go up the street. The hospital is on
    the left.

Track 68

a MAN: Excuse me. Where's the library?
BEEP
MAN: Thank you.

b WOMAN: Excuse me. Is there a supermarket near here?
BEEP
WOMAN: Thanks.

c MAN: Excuse me. Where's the cinema?
BEEP
MAN: Thank you.

d WOMAN: Excuse me. Where's the town hall?
BEEP
WOMAN: Thanks.

Track 69

a YOUNG MAN: Is there a hospital in this town?
OLD WOMAN: Yes, there is. It's near the car park.

b YOUNG WOMAN: Are there any supermarkets near here?
YOUNG MAN: Yes, there are. There are two.

c MAN: Where is the town hall?
WOMAN: There isn't a town hall here.

Track 70

a supermarket
b car park
c shopping centre
d sports centre

Track 71

a YOUNG WOMAN: May I turn the music down?
OLDER MAN: Yes, of course. It's very loud.

b YOUNG MAN: Do you mind if I open the window?
OLDER WOMAN: No, I don't. Go ahead.

c YOUNG MAN: Can I go to Joe's party tonight?
MUM: No, you can't. You have school tomorrow.

d YOUNG WOMAN: Do you mind if I watch the TV?
OLDER MAN: That's fine. See if there's a good programme.

e YOUNG MAN: Can I borrow your car?
YOUNG WOMAN: OK, but I need it this afternoon.

f YOUNG WOMAN: Can I listen to your CDs?
YOUNG MAN: Sure. Find something you like.

Track 72

a YOUNG WOMAN: May I turn the music down?
BEEP

b BEEP
OLDER WOMAN: No, I don't. Go ahead.

c YOUNG MAN: Can I go to Joe's party tonight?
BEEP

d BEEP
OLDER MAN: That's fine. See if there's a good programme.

e YOUNG MAN: Can I borrow your car?
BEEP

f BEEP
YOUNG MAN: Sure. Find something you like.

Track 73

a YOUNG WOMAN: Can you play the guitar?
YOUNG MAN: Yes, I can.

b YOUNG MAN: Can you play the trumpet?
YOUNG WOMAN: No, I can't, but I can play the violin.

c YOUNG WOMAN: Can you read music?
YOUNG MAN: No, I can't, but I can sing.

Track 74

a Can you sing?
b Yes, I can.
c No, I can't.
d She can't see.

Track 75

a I have to wait in the gym.
I have two weights in the gym.

b They don't have two plays in the theatre.
They don't have to play in the theatre.

c She has two works in the museum.
She has to work in the museum.

Track 76

a YOUNG WOMAN: Can you lend me a book?
YOUNG MAN: OK. This one is great – it's a really interesting story.

b YOUNG MAN: Can I borrow a pencil?
YOUNG WOMAN: Sorry. I only have one and I'm using it.

c YOUNG WOMAN: Can I borrow your car?
YOUNG MAN: Sorry. I have to drive my grandmother to the shops.

d YOUNG MAN: Can you lend me a jacket?
YOUNG WOMAN: Sure. I have a sweater I can wear.

Track 77

a YOUNG WOMAN: Can you lend me a book?
BEEP

b BEEP
YOUNG WOMAN: Sorry. I only have one and I'm using it.

c YOUNG WOMAN: Can I borrow your car?
BEEP

d BEEP
YOUNG WOMAN: Sure. I have a sweater I can wear.

Track 78

a Physics
b Chemistry
c Biology
d Maths
e Geography
f History

Track 79

JODY: Mark! Have you seen my umbrella?
MARK: I think it's next to the door.
JODY: No, my keys are there, but I can't find my umbrella.
MARK: Is it in the bathroom?
JODY: Oh yes, that's right. Thanks.

FRANK: Excuse me. Is there a post office near here?
MARTHA: Hmmm. Yes, there is. Go straight down this street, then turn right and the post office is on the left opposite the town hall.
FRANK: Thanks.

SUZANNA: Where are my keys?
JAMES: They're on the table.
SUZANNA: No, they aren't.
JAMES: Are they under that book?
SUZANNA: Oh yes, thanks. They're on the chair.
OLD LADY: Excuse me. Are there any restaurants near here?

YOUNG MAN: Yes, there are two. There's one next to the cinema on the left and there's one between the supermarket and the library on the right.

OLD LADY: Thank you.

Track 80

Plurals that end in the sound /s/: banks, car parks, clarinets, desks, lamps, parks, restaurants, stamps, supermarkets, toilets, trumpets,

Plurals that end in the sound /z/: bars, bass guitars, bathrooms, bedrooms, beds, bicycles, chairs, clubs, computers, dining rooms, drums, guitars, gyms, harmonicas, hospitals, kitchens, keyboards, libraries, living rooms, museums, pianos, rugs, saxophones, showers, schools, shopping centres, sofas, swimming pools, tables, town halls, TVs, umbrellas, violins,

Plurals that end in the sound /iz/: bridges, fridges, post offices,

Track 81

Words that have the sound /r/:
bathroom
bedroom
bridge
Chemistry
clarinet
country
drums
fridge
Geography
History
library
restaurant
rug
trumpet
umbrella

Track 82

a Don't touch that!
b Keep off the grass!
c Look out! There's a mouse on the table!
d Mind the dog!

Track 83

a Don't touch that!
   BEEP
b Look out! There's a mouse on the table!
   BEEP
c Mind the dog!
   BEEP
d Keep off the grass!
   BEEP

Track 84

a mouse   mouse
b mouse   mice
c mice   mice
d high   how
e how   how
f high   high

Track 85

a mouse
b rhino

c penguin
d wild animal
e be careful
f look out

Track 86

a MAN: Do you like snow?
   WOMAN: No, I hate cold weather.
b MAN: Do you like cloudy weather?
   WOMAN: Yes, it's lovely.
c MAN: I love the sunshine.
   WOMAN: I don't. I hate hot weather.
d MAN: I love the rain.
   WOMAN: Oh really? I don't. It's awful.

Track 87

I love watching TV. It's great!
BEEP
Oh really? What about sports? Do you like sports?
BEEP
That's interesting. Do you want to go out in the rain? Do you like the rain?
BEEP
Ok. What about hot weather? Do you like it?
BEEP

Track 88

N.B Speaker gives stress and intonation only of the following
a (That's terrible!)
b (That's great!)
c (I love hot weather!)
d (I hate cold weather!)
e (It was awful!)
f (It was lovely!)

Track 89

a That's terrible!
b That's great!
c I love hot weather!
d I hate cold weather!
e It was awful!
f It was lovely!

Track 90

a terrible
b awful
c lovely
d sunny
e raining
f cloudy

Track 91

a played, turned, lived, liked. Liked is different, liked.
b kissed cooked died watched. Died is different, died.
c wanted, beheaded, washed, decided. Washed is different, washed.
d arrived, reached, loved, divorced. Reached is different, reached.
e landed, ended, lifted, happened. Happened is different, happened.
f started, worked , baked, walked. Started is different, started.

Track 92

Verbs with /d/: played, turned, lived, died, arrived, loved, happened

Verbs with /t/: liked, divorced, kissed, cooked, watched, washed, reached, worked, baked, walked

Verbs with /ɪd/: wanted, beheaded, decided, landed, ended, lifted, started

Track 93

WOMAN: Who was Yuri Gagarin?

BEEP

WOMAN: What do you know about his career?

BEEP

WOMAN: Wow! What happened after that? Did he go round the Earth again?

BEEP

WOMAN: Oh no! That's sad.

Track 94

a war

b soldier

c independence

d moon

e finally

f banana

Track 95

MAN: Hi! How's it going?

WOMAN: Fine thanks. You?

MAN: Great. Did you have a good holiday?

WOMAN: Yes, we did. It was fun.

MAN: Well, I have to go. It was nice to talk to you.

WOMAN: You too. See you around.

MAN: Yes, bye.

Track 96

a BEEP

   WOMAN: Fine, thanks.

b BEEP

   WOMAN: Yes, thank you. Everybody's fine. What about your family?

c BEEP

   WOMAN: Nice to see you too. Let's get together some time.

d BEEP

   WOMAN: Yes, give me a call.

e BEEP

   WOMAN: Bye. See you soon.

Track 97

a Pass the pepper please.

b Can you write that later?

c We didn't sell the boat.

d I can't believe he failed.

e I have a pain in my hand.

Track 98

a underground

b London

c foot

d caravan

e convertible

Track 99

KATYA: Hi! How are you?

BEEP

KATYA: Well, on Sunday we went to a safari park.

BEEP

KATYA: Yes, we like safari parks too. First we saw lions and a rhino. We took lots of photos.

BEEP

KATYA: Next we went to see the monkeys.

BEEP

KATYA: Oh, I like monkeys but they climbed all over the car.

BEEP

KATYA: Then they broke the mirrors.

BEEP

KATYA: Well, John called for help. Finally, the guards came and helped us.

BEEP

KATYA: Yes, call me. And you can see my photos!

BEEP

Track 100

Verbs with the sound /t/

cook – cooked, jump – jumped, kiss – kissed, laugh – laughed, look – looked, wash – washed, watch – watched

Verbs with the sound /ɪd/

behead – beheaded, decide – decided, end – ended, invite – invited, want – wanted

Verbs with the sound /d/ breathe – breathed, die – died, love – loved, play – played, practise – practised, travel – travelled, turn – turned

Track 101

Words with the sound /ɑɪ/: mice, white, tigers, July

Words with the sound /ɑʊ/: mouse, house, brown, now

Words with the sound /e/: pepper, ketchup, let's, bread, get, many

Words with the sound /eɪ/: waiter, steak, hey, paid, babies

Track 102

a The plural of mouse is mice. What's the plural of house?

b Waiter! Can I have some pepper and ketchup for my steak?

c Hey, let's have white bread, not brown.

d Can I get paid now?

e How many tigers had babies in July?

Track 103

Conversation 1

WOMAN: Where are you?

MAN: I'm lost.

WOMAN: What can you see?

MAN: Well, the sea, of course. I'm on a beach with lots of trees at the bottom of a cliff.

WOMAN: Are you near a cave?

MAN: erm … yes, I can see a cave near here.

WOMAN: OK. I know where you are. Don't move. I'm coming.

Conversation 2

WOMAN: Where are you?

MAN: I'm lost.

WOMAN: What can you see?

MAN: Well, the sea, of course and a beach. I'm in a forest, near a river, on a mountain.

WOMAN: Are you near a village?

MAN: No, but I can see one far, far away.

WOMAN: OK. I know where you are. Don't move. I'm coming.

Track 104

a Sit down and eat your meat.

b Please take a seat, Phil.

c Tim's team is going to win.

d Listen and fill in the blanks on your sheet.

e This machine's very quick.

Track 105

a I have a stomach ache.
BEEP

b I have an English test tomorrow.
BEEP

c Thank you very much for my present.
BEEP

d We're going to visit your country!
BEEP

e We're going to be there in July. Is it going to rain, do you think?
BEEP

f Do you think we're going to like the food?
BEEP

Track 106

a hope

b village

c treasure

d tomorrow

e fingers

Track 107

MAN: What shall we do on Saturday?

WOMAN: Why don't we go to the cinema?

MAN: Is there anything good on?

WOMAN: There's a Japanese film on at the local cinema.

MAN: That sounds interesting. Let's do that.

WOMAN: Shall I go and buy the tickets?

MAN: You don't have to go and buy the tickets. You can buy them on the phone.

WOMAN: That's a good idea.

Track 108

IRINA: Wow! It's the weekend, finally! What are you going to do tomorrow?
BEEP

IRINA: That sounds good. What are your plans for Sunday?
BEEP

IRINA: I'm going to go to a pop concert.
BEEP

IRINA: Shall we talk again next week?
BEEP

IRINA: Well, have a good weekend!
BEEP

Track 109

a Aren't you going to answer the phone?

b There's going to be a jazz concert in September.

c I'm going to ask Jamie to come.

d Who are you going to invite?

e Where are The Urban Rats going to play?

f When is the new gallery going to open?

Track 110

a gallery

b cafeteria

c restaurant

d theatre

e entertainment

Track 111

JESPER: Where shall we have the party, on the beach?

ELLA: No, it's too hot.

JESPER: In the house?

ELLA: The house isn't big enough.

JESPER: What about the garden then?

ELLA: Yes, the garden is better. It's large enough. And it's cooler than the beach.

JESPER: OK, the garden then. Shall we have Indian food?

ELLA: Oh no, it's too spicy.

JESPER: Italian?

ELLA: Hmm, too boring.

JESPER: How about a barbecue? Is that exciting enough?

ELLA: Yes, that sounds nice.

JESPER: Great, let's send the invitations.

ELLA: It's too soon. Let's wait a bit.

Track 112

MAN: What kind of movie do you want to see, a romantic comedy, a western or an action film?
BEEP

MAN: What time shall we go, at 2.00pm, 6.00pm or 10.00pm?
BEEP

MAN: Shall we go to a restaurant after?
BEEP

MAN: OK. Do you want to walk or take a taxi? Or shall we take our bikes?
BEEP

MAN: OK. See you later.

Track 113

a Beaches are hotter than mountains.

b This book's more interesting than that one.

c Bob's shorter than Peter.

d He's more attractive than Peter.

e Miranda's as clever as Tim.

f Today's better than yesterday and not as good as tomorrow.

Track 114

a buying

b prettier

c unattractive

d beautiful

Track 115

a I think robots that clean the house are a really good idea. What do you think?
BEEP

b Computers are better than people. They don't make mistakes, don't you agree?
BEEP

c Big, fast cars in big cities are a really bad idea, don't you think?
BEEP

d I think cycling is better than driving. Do you agree with me?
   BEEP
e Space travel doesn't do anything good for people.
   BEEP
f Listen to this in the paper: Computer games are bad for children. Do you agree with that?
   BEEP

Track 116
Words with the sound /e/
bed men ten wedding
Words with the sound /æ/
bad cat man marry tan
Words with the sound /ʌ/
cut does love money won
Words with the sound /ɜ:/
bird turn word work world

Track 117
a ago
b digital
c technology
d palmtop
e interview

Track 118
WOMAN: What are your plans for next Saturday?
BEEP
SAMIRA: That's nice. Where is it going to be?
BEEP
SAMIRA: Are they going to have a reception?
BEEP
SAMIRA: Is it going to be at their house?
BEEP
SAMIRA: Are you going to buy them a present?
BEEP
SAMIRA: Do you have time for a coffee before the party?
BEEP
SAMIRA: Well, have a good time!

Track 119
SAMIRA: What shall I wear to the wedding?
JAMES: Why don't you wear your white dress?
SAMIRA: Only the bride wears white. She's more important than all the other women that day, so I think that's right, don't you agree?
JAMES: No, I don't agree. That's silly.
SAMIRA: You're wrong!
JAMES: Oh, it isn't important.
SAMIRA: You're right. Let's agree to disagree.
SAMIRA: What are you going to wear to the wedding?
JAMES: Jeans, a T-shirt and a jacket.
SAMIRA: That's not nice enough for a wedding.
JAMES: OK. Jeans, a shirt and a jacket?
SAMIRA: Hmm I suppose.
SAMIRA: Is the wedding going to be fun?
NICOLE: I hope so.
SAMIRA: Are you going to have children soon?
NICOLE: I hope not!
SAMIRA: Are you planning to live in this area?
NICOLE: Well, it's very expensive but I hope we can find a cheap flat. Keep your fingers crossed!

Track 120
MAN: Dear friends, we are celebrating today Paul and Nicole's new life together. I met Paul on our first day at high school. We did everything together. We studied together, we had fun together and we didn't fall in love together, but at the same time. One day he said: 'Do you remember Nicole from high school?' He didn't have to say more. I knew this was real love. So, in the future I'm going to do everything with Paul AND Nicole! And the first thing we are going to do is drink to their happiness. Nicole and Paul.

Track 121
Words with the sound /i:/: beach, eat, peace, sea
Words with the sound /ɪ/: cliff, digital, disk, picnic, river
Words with the sound /e/: check-up, contestant, memory, health, press, treasure
Words with the sound /æ/: crash, match, plans, plasma, narrow
Words with the sound /ʌ/: bungee, check-up, club, cutlery, jump
Words with the sound /ɜ:/: concert, detergent, earn, modern service

Track 122
a My car's older than yours. I'm going to buy a new one.
b This room's hotter than the Sahara! I'm going to open the windows.
c This film's more interesting than the others. I'm going to ask Molly to come.
d This camera's not as good as that one. I'm going to get a digital one.